POETRY AND MATHEMATICS

Poetry
and
Mathematics

❦ ❦ ❦ ❦ ❦

by SCOTT BUCHANAN
With a new Introduction

J. B. Lippincott Company
Philadelphia
and New York

CONTENTS

AUTHOR'S NOTE

THIS BOOK MIGHT BE DEDICATED to the proposition that each human being is both a poet and a mathematician, but perhaps it might better be dedicated to two human beings who were superb masters of poetry and mathematics, Dante and Kepler. Dante constructed the *Divine Comedy* on a framework of Aristotelian and Ptolemaic astronomy. Kepler transformed this framework into the modern solar system. Both were guided by the poetic considerations of theological, psychological, and moral analogies. (See the chapter on Proportions.)

The woodcut on page 9, which also appears, in slightly different form, on the cover of this book, is from the original edition of Kepler's *Mysterium Cosmographicum*. It is a diagram of the solar system or cosmos constructed with six concentric spheres spaced and held apart by five regular solids. The outer sphere is the sphere of Saturn, the next the sphere of Jupiter, the next the sphere of Mars, the next the sphere of Earth, the next the sphere of Venus, and the next the sphere of Mercury. (Only the first four spheres are visible in the diagram; the others can be imagined.) The five regular solids are (reading from outside to inside):

The cube, consisting of six squares
The tetrahedron or pyramid, consisting of four equilateral triangles
The dodecahedron, consisting of twelve regular pentagons
The icosahedron, consisting of twenty equilateral triangles
The octahedron, consisting of eight equilateral triangles

For Kepler the mystery arose from the following considerations: (1) that only these five regular solids were possible; (2) that there were six planets; (3) that thus successively inscribed in spheres the regular solids determined the correct diameters of the spheres to contain the orbits of the planets as observed by Tycho Brahe and calculated by Kepler.

The mysterious diagram was first constructed and explained in the *Mysterium Cosmographicum* in 1596, then repeated in the *Harmonies of the World* in 1616 after all the corrections and revisions in the orbits had been worked out in the *Epitome of Copernican Astronomy*. It had been the guiding vision throughout.

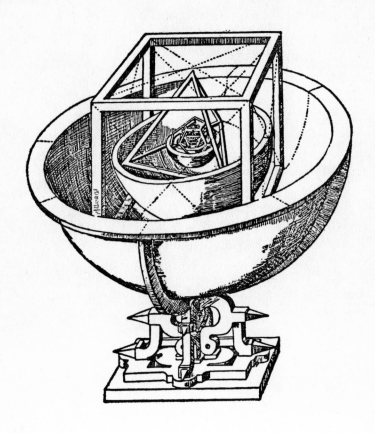

A NEW INTRODUCTION

THE OCCASION OF A NEW EDITION of this peculiar book offers an opportunity for the writer to say in a new introduction how the idea of it originally occurred and what some of its consequences have been. After the book was written the idea was recognized by one of the more learned readers to be the idea of the seven liberal arts. The consequences have been a radical reform of teaching and learning in a small province of the modern academy.

From 1925 to 1929 I was the Assistant Director of the People's Institute in New York City. When I joined it, the Institute was thirty years old, having been established by Charles Sprague Smith, a professor of comparative literature at Columbia University. He had suddenly seen the parts of his professed subject matter articulated and made concrete in the life of the metropolis. In simple terms, he wanted the immigrants of the lower East Side to meet the intellectuals of the upper West Side, to make the "melting pot" boil, to make one culture out of many under the aegis of an unused article in the Charter of Cooper Union. Peter Cooper's intention was that the training in the mechanical arts at Cooper Union should be in part balanced by lectures in the Great Hall on social and political ethics. The formality had to be stretched to cover Smith's purposes, but this was enthusiastically done by the trustees because they were all too painfully aware that they had been unable to carry out the purpose of the founder except on special occasions such as when Abraham Lincoln had delivered his famous Cooper Union address in the Great Hall.

In its thirty years the People's Institute had had a rather remarkable career in American popular education. As the earlier Lyceum and Chautauqua had brought itinerant scientific and literary teachers to urban and rural centers of population, so the People's Institute had brought in people from distant places and traditions to hear lectures twice a week on literature, politics, economics, and society in free open assembly. From the start there had been questions and discussion from the floor following each lecture, and these exercises had brought sharp and sometimes learned criticism and dialectic to bear upon the lectures. It was fully recognized that European cultures had migrated to these shores with the immigrants, and that assimilation to American ways was not the only transaction that took place in the melting pot. At one stage the Institute took pains to set up separate centers where imported arts and crafts, which languished in the industry and commerce of the city, could be revived and promoted to help civilize the American community. There were annual fairs for the exhibition of their products. The lectures, literary and academic as they might be in origin, took account of events here and abroad, so that by the time of World War I the Great Hall not only boiled; it often exploded verbally, on occasion violently, with the issues of the times. It was a true forum.

In 1925 there was an established schedule of three lectures a week: on Sunday evenings lectures on politics and morals, on Tuesday evenings lectures on natural and social science, and on Friday evenings a series of lectures by Everett Dean Martin, the Director. During the war Martin had been editorial analyst of the news for the New York *Tribune*. His special contribution had been the application of the psychological doctrines of William James, Freud, and Le Bon to the deeper issues of the world war. Before the war Martin had been a soapboxer in Chicago and before that a Congregational preacher in Des Moines. He was an authentic orator in the tradition of teaching and preaching of Emerson, Bryan, and Ingersoll. His secret was a sensitive attention to his audience; he never launched his theme until he had established rapport with his audience, and he accomplished this by humorous provocation. He had established a deep enduring rapport with the People's Institute audience through several years of lectures, variations on a developing psychological theory of social revolutions in world history. He had the ambition and the learning capacity to become a philosopher of history. The pervading theme of his lectures was liberty, the internal freedom from passion and dogma as the aim of liberal education, individual freedom from mass pressures, and political freedom against tyrannical governments and institutions. Certain lectures each year celebrated the same heroes, Socrates, Cicero, Rousseau, Tom Paine, and Jefferson. This repeated series of lectures had become a curriculum or, perhaps better, the syllabus for an as yet nonexistent curriculum which was being demanded by the students.

This demand for more study was the best evidence that learning was already taking place. Though the Martin series was backed by the Tuesday and Sunday lectures, given annually by about fifty literary, academic, and scientific lecturers who had become familiar to the students, the students wanted also shorter series of lectures for smaller audiences, to dig deeper into psychology, economics, history, natural science, medicine, philosophy, and literature.

It would be quite misleading to think of this center of teaching and learning as a mission to the slums. Certain members of the audience were noticeable as underprivileged slum dwellers who found a free lecture a physically and socially warm place to take a nap. But the great body of the audience was first- or second-generation immigrants whose migration to this country had uprooted them from intellectual and educational traditions which they had come to fear they would lose in America. These were sharply critical, often scolding the lecturer for sentimental or sloppy reasoning. There were also the internal migrants, remnants of native American intellectual and political movements, who spent their summers in harvesting on the Great Plains or in lumber camps, and who rode the rods back to New York for the winter. Some of these were continuing the reading and discussion which had started when they knew Jack London. One could always find them during the day conversing and smoking, in the lobby of the reading room of the New York Public Library, at Fifth Avenue and Forty-second Street. These two groups, the East Siders and the Wobblies, as we used to call them, were with the graduate students from the local universities at that time probably the best read audience in America. They were not reading and studying for degrees and advancement in life, but to know and to understand. The People's Institute and the Public Library provided them with the opportunity of higher education without requiring credits and degrees or the promise of jobs. The Institute was not initiating, coercing, cajoling, or finishing education, as schools and colleges are wont to do.

It happened at this time that Frederick Keppel, former Dean at Columbia and then president of the Carnegie Corporation, was try-ing to persuade his trustees that a new attempt at adult education for the country was called for. He recognized in the People's Institute, as well as in the Labor Temple under Will Durant, and the New School for Social Research under Alvin Johnson, models for the organization of education across the country. So the Carnegie Corporation gave a grant to the People's Institute to set up the extra lectures and to explore the use of the Great Books. At the same time the Carnegie Corporation made grants to promote a new American Association for Adult Education.

My assignment as Assistant Director of the Institute was to help arrange the single lectures on Sunday and Tuesday evenings at Cooper Union, to find the best way to meet the demand for extra lecture series first at the Manhattan Trade School and then at the Muhlenburg Branch of the Public Library, and to explore the possibilities of seminar and tutorial work for still smaller and advanced groups. This was a very exciting job for a new Ph.D. who with his fellow graduate students had been appalled at the low state of the intellectual arts in the conventional college or university department of philosophy. From observing workers' education in England I had surmised that the lively edge of learning had moved outside academic walls and beyond the grasp of the formal disciplines. As chairman and organizer of lectures, I confirmed the guess in the question and discussion periods. New York City in the 'twenties was certainly a cave of the winds of doctrine, and I soon became one of those blown about in it.

It seemed to me that the function of the People's Institute and other centers like it was to precipitate insights and understanding, perhaps to find centers of calm in the storm. One such attempt is memorable. Some of the students formed a club to continue discussions after the lectures in an abandoned artist's studio on Twenty-second Street. This was to take the place of many small Kaffee-klatsches in the night life of the Childs Restaurants of the time. It turned into long sessions around the samovar with tea glasses and copies of Marx's *Capital,* Spinoza's *Ethics,* and St. Thomas's *Summa,* then in its first English translation, lying at hand. And these heated disputations were only the foci of discussions of Greek tragedy, Stoic ethics, Aristotelian, atomic, and energetic physics, Dante's *Divine Comedy,* Milton's *Paradise Lost,* Newtonian and Einsteinian space, Humian and Kantian epistemology, Hegelian and Spenglerian theories of history, Russian novels, and Oriental epics. These in turn were only the deeper background of the Russian Revolution, the anarchist co-operative theories, the spectrum of socialisms, and the cults of Freemasonry, Rosicrucianism, theosophy, the single tax, Herbert Spencer, Walt Whitman and Emerson. The liveliest foreground consisted of the reporters or popularizers of the new physics, Eddington, Russell, Whitehead, and Bridgman. These discussions were never formalized with assignments of topics to leaders; the man with the latest book under his arm usually took over for the evening after the lecture had had its going over.

From this club and from a few other centers, one the Café Royal on Second Avenue, where a dozen of us met weekly to discuss our reading of Plato's *Dialogues,* I got the information and the feel of learning which guided me in choosing lecturers and topics. After two or three years of thirty weeks of this kind of work and long vacations to think it over I began to see some form in the chaos and to make some judgments. One of these was that we ought to accept Mortimer Adler's advice to use the Columbia Honors Course in Great Books for seminars in the branches of the Public Library. Another was that I should provide some basic teaching in two "subjects" that seemed to be missing in the minds of these students. One subject was mathematics, ignorance of which was proving a real barrier to communication and understanding. The other was poetry or poetics, the free use of the imagination as an auxiliary to abstract doctrine.

I tried to get academic help in providing the right elementary instruction. This proved an almost insuperable difficulty, and in the course of the search and a few trials and errors, I happened on something of a discovery, at least for me. Our academic education with all its formalization and sophistication does not deal with the elements of its subject matters; furthermore the teacher in primary and secondary education as well as in college and university does not know what the elements of his subject matter are. I later learned that the great German mathematician Klein had delivered a series of lectures to teachers of mathematics in Germany, entitled *Elementary Mathematics from the Higher Standpoint*. If I had known this at the time, I might have found a better solution than I did. But I was driven back to trying to do it myself, to finding some pedagogic way of providing the elements of mathematics and poetry that would bring effective order into a lively learning situation. I announced in advance a series of lectures under the title of the present book, and then spent a summer in preparation.

The summer was spent in preparing myself rather than the lectures themselves. I had been a teacher of mathematics in a high school at one time, and at another a teacher of Greek, and I had majored in both in college, but I was neither a mathematician nor a poet. Later work in the philosophy of mathematics perhaps gave me some advantage in trying to hunt for the elements, the building blocks from which the delicate structures of both subjects are made. But I found myself forever circling around and never capturing the things I sought. I was like the blind men in the familiar anecdote of the elephant; they could not identify the legs, the trunk, and the tail of the elephant except as trees, snake, and rope because they had no sight of the animal of which these were parts. So the numbers, figures, equations, and functions of mathematics, and the narratives, characters, plots, and styles of poetry wove for me illusory patterns, and my reach exceeded my grasp.

It was only when I actually gave the lectures to a small and sympathetic audience that I found stable patterns, although not the elements that I sought. Much to my surprise, I found that mathematics and poetry run parallel patterns, such that one illuminates the other. A puzzle in one has a corresponding puzzle in the other, and sometimes, though not always, they can be understood together when they are unintelligible apart. Ordinary language attests to the connection, as when one counts numbers and recounts a story, or when geometrical figures are compared with figures of speech, or when in Greek the word for ratio is *analogon,* or when physiological functions can be expressed in mathematical functions. There are dangers in this etymological game, as I learned when a word led me astray, but there is also confirmation of many guesses if the faith in words is boldly followed. At any rate I finished the projected lectures, probably with more learning on my part than illumination for my patient listeners. I later wrote this book from the notes for the lectures. It probably contains more of the discussion that followed the lectures than of the original delivery. The style shows that.

The attentive reader will see that after sometimes laborious and sometimes fantastic searches I was able to come to rather simple conclusions about the poetic and mathematical elements. The symbolic elements of poetry are words, and the corresponding elements of mathematics are ratios. It is rather easy to pass from these symbolic elements to the aspects of reality which they designate. Words stand for qualities; ratios stand for relations. Qualities in relation can be built by *ratio-cination* into the structures of poetry and mathematics, into the worlds that tragedies and comedies comprehend. But clear as such a conclusion can be made, it floats like a nebula in space, or like a cloud in the wind. It begs for context and substantiation. The elements seem to be fictions.

There were present at the lectures and in the usual conversations that followed two friends from Columbia University who also gave lectures and led discussions at the People's Institute, Mortimer Adler and Richard McKeon. McKeon had just returned from work with Etienne Gilson at the Sorbonne and was rapidly setting up shop in medieval philosophy. When *Poetry and Mathematics* was written, McKeon supplied its context. He insisted that I had stumbled into a rediscovery of the seven liberal arts, the trivium—grammar, rhetoric and logic—and the quadrivium—arithmetic, geometry, music and astronomy. He further insisted that we three ought to proceed with a revision of the traditional forms and a reconstruction of them for the sake of the order and articulation they could bring to the contemporary college and university. We also speculated on the possibility of making a modern trivium and quadrivium the basis of a curriculum for a People's University which would result if there were a merger of the New School for Social Research, the Labor Temple, and the People's Institute.

Mark Van Doren, another lecturer, reminded us of the legend of the Seven Sleepers, the Muses of the Liberal Arts who sometimes sleep for centuries in a cave under Mount Helicon, to be awakened on occasion by a wandering shepherd boy playing his pipes. He later wrote a poem celebrating the occasion, in which he adds prophetically that a long journey sometimes has to be made to reach Mount Helicon across centuries and continents.

The three of us, accompanied then and later by an increasing number, including Van Doren, Robert Hutchins, and Stringfellow Barr, undertook this journey. The first year Adler, McKeon, and I gave a series of lectures at Cooper Union on the traditional structure of a university, using the forms of the original European universities and filling them with the content of modern learning. For the sake of clarity we kept the old terminology, poetry divided into grammar, rhetoric and logic; mathematics divided into arithmetic, geometry, music, and astronomy. The modern mathematical content fits into the traditional forms pretty much as the five middle chapters of this book, figures, numbers, ratios and proportions, equations and functions, correspond to the quadrivium. The poetic content is well revised to fit the trivium: grammar, rhetoric, and logic. These seven liberal arts, the two divisions paralleling each other, form the trunk of the tree of knowledge. The three-branched top of the tree divides into the traditional professional subject matters, medicine, law, and theology. This gave us the diagrammatic syllabus for the lectures.

It may seem that the Great Hall of Cooper Union was a peculiar place to deliver such lectures, whose contents were abstract and academic. As we have learned since then, it was a peculiarly fitting place. We had shared our own learning with the audience and they had shared theirs with us, so that the utopian university that we described brought a kind of order to our common experience, a kind of order that has proved anathema to the conventional academic establishments in this country. A rather large minority of the audience understood and followed our first groping formulations of a basic organization of modern knowledge for institutional teaching and learning, and they followed it with enthusiasm. Those who did not understand, or who disagreed joined in the controversial discussion.

Fortunately, with the help of Philip Youtz the People's Institute had by then followed the recommendation of Mortimer Adler that we should bring the Honors Course in Great Books to the branches of the Public Library in New York City. The American Library Association published a small handbook giving the list of great books with a supplementary bibliography. Youtz set up eighteen seminars in the branch libraries, each to be taught or led by pairs of young instructors or recent graduates of Columbia College. Similar seminars had comprised the Honors Course for selected students in Columbia College under the leadership and administration of John Erskine.

In the earlier days Erskine, Mark Van Doren, Raymond Weaver, Mortimer Adler, and others had been the teachers. The original list of books had come from Sir John Lubbock, who had edited it for Kegan, Paul, London publishers, for use in the Workers' and Mechanics' Institutes in England in the 'eighties.

The library seminars flourished, some still exist. Our study of the formal liberal arts began to throw light on the books. A great book is the product of the liberal arts; the authors are liberal artists, masters of the arts. The great books improve the mind because they induce the formal habits of learning in the reader and discussant. The aim of the liberal arts is insight, understanding, imagination, and finally the transformation of the student into his own teacher and the teacher of others. The result of liberal education is lifelong learning and teaching. The social fruit of the tree of knowledge is an intellectual culture. The rediscovery of the liberal arts could be the much-needed beginning of the reconstruction of education in this country.

But the 'twenties in New York City, as elsewhere, were drawing to a close; the fateful year, 1929, arrived. As many remember, the 'twenties were a kind of flash renaissance in American if not world culture. There was a release of speculative energy, financial, artistic, intellectual, which marks the period as a kind of high-water mark in freedom of speech, of thought, and of experimentation. But it could not last, and everything that has happened since has seemed like some phase of the great Depression that began in 1929. I have never known how to judge whether the financial depression was cause or effect or concomitant of a general decline of the human spirit. The period of the New Deal seems only a cultural fever with hopes of a cure for deep spiritual illness.

At any rate, 1929 was the year when there were rumors that the trustees of the Carnegie Corporation were being persuaded that the American adult education movement should not concentrate its efforts on the merely intellectual arts; it would have to serve a broad spectrum of human needs, including basic economic welfare, and human desires such as entertainment. There were also rumors that Cooper Union was about to settle a long bout of litigation concerning the rental income from the land on which the Chrysler Building stood, an income that would amount to a large increase in endowment. Cooper Union would then take over the functions of the People's Institute and administer them as a department of social philosophy. These rumors were not to become facts for some time, but they coincided with my own sense that the enterprises the People's Institute had fostered should be carried on elsewhere; the idea of a people's university might well be reintroduced to the conventional university.

I therefore accepted an invitation to join the philosophy department at the University of Virginia. This also meant that I would be rejoining my old friend, Stringfellow Barr, who was teaching history and editing the *Virginia Quarterly Review* there. He and I had spent long hours in talk about the plight of American education when we were both Rhodes Scholars at Oxford, he from Virginia and I from Massachusetts.

Mortimer Adler, who had been working with Robert Hutchins on the law of evidence at the Yale Law School, decided to carry the great books and the liberal arts to the University of Chicago. Richard McKeon was shortly to go from Columbia to Chicago, where he soon became Dean of the Humanities, but for the time being he stayed on in New York, where he lent part of his time to helping Everett Martin arrange the People's Institute lectures, which were soon to be terminated.

So 1929 was the year of dispersal and transplantation for our idea of the liberal arts. The new soils for the seedlings proved both energizing and hostile. Very soon Hutchins and Adler conceived and proposed the establishment of an Institute of Philosophical Studies where the liberal arts and the professions would be studied with the aim of formulating a new plan for American colleges and universities. It was even imagined that such an institute would be a model for imitation by other colleges and universities, a sort of permanently institutionalized curriculum committee to act as receiver for the elective curricular systems that were showing signs of bankruptcy all over the country. But the departmental principalities and powers at the University of Chicago chose to see this as a power conspiracy on the part of the administration, which was pictured as a "baby president," aided by Savonarola and Richelieu. The shock of the picture brought out a formal countervailing power, the Stop Hutchins Committee of elder academic politicians. Such is the habitual transformation of speculative enterprises into power conspiracies in all American universities. The University of Chicago has always been the great arena for such spectacles, the most illustrious case being the occasion around the turn of the century, when John Dewey resigned to go to Columbia.

Stringfellow Barr and I quickly picked up our conversations where we had left off, and the University of Virginia was a fertile field for participant observation as well as speculation. The college at the University was being squeezed, exploited, and reduced to the size and functions of a secondary preparatory school for the graduate schools, which were in turn losing their professional statuses and becoming handmaidens to the going concerns of science, technology, and business. The superficial symptoms of the dis-ease appeared as worries about the better undergraduate students who were not getting liberal arts training commensurate with their powers. It was reported that an *ad hoc* Honors Course for the better students had been chosen by only two and a half students per year, one of those statistical monstrosities of computerized dean's offices. President Alderman set up a committee to study the problem and make recommendations. Barr and I were members.

But the conversations that were becoming formal and heated in this enterprise were soon interrupted by a reader of *Poetry and Mathematics*, Ethel S. Dummer of Chicago. On reading the book she had guessed that I might be the person who would help her in her study of the writings of George Boole, the mathematician, and his wife, Mary Boole. George Boole had been the first holder of the chair in mathematics at the University of Cork, a chair which by charter must be filled by a self-taught mathematician. He fitted the chair to a T since he had won Royal Society medals, but held no degrees. He had written, among others, two remarkable books, one on *Differential Equations*, which is still a standard reference, and another, *The Laws of Thought*, in which algebra had been generalized into one of the styles of mathematical logic which is now used in mechanical computers and cybernetics. The last chapter of *The Laws of Thought* discusses in tentative and suggestive style the constitution of the human mind which is able to solve differential equations and generalize the method to all thought. Mary Boole, a nonprofessional mathematician in her own right, had gone on after her husband's early death to explore the hypotheses and suggestions of this last chapter. She had by chance learned some of the operational interpretation of algebra and also the Augustinian doctrine of intellectual intuition as the method of mathematical discovery. She was convinced that her husband, George, practiced the operational art while holding the mystical doctrine concerning his own inspiration. Through her acquaintance with James Hinton and her own teaching of mathematics she had stumbled on the hypothesis of the unconscious mind long before the Freudian doctrine was known.

I accepted Mrs. Dummer's invitation to spend a year in England digging up the context that would interpret the Booles' somewhat mysterious adventures in mathematics and poetry.

I soon discovered that context in the intellectual ferment that had accompanied the acceptance by British mathematicians, after a hundred and fifty years of idolatrous and patriotic fidelity to the name of Newton and the literal scriptures of fluxions, of the Leibnitzian and Continental notation for the calculus. This breach of the traditional insularity of Britain had, like others before and after, set off a tidal wave of science and thought. The break had been made by a small junta of Cambridge mathematicians, Herschel, Peacock, Babbage, and De Morgan, who called themselves the Analytic Society. By the translation of French mathematical texts, the elaboration of the study of series, the invention of other calculuses, and, perhaps most important, the exposition of calculuses of operations, they had teased, cajoled, instructed, and persuaded their colleagues. It was in this context that George Boole had taught himself and made his original contributions. It was no wonder that he had been dazzled by his own discoveries and that Mary Boole had caught the brilliant rays in her eyes.

I was struck by the undercurrent of worry in the writings of these men, a worry about the luxurious use of mathematical analogy in which they had indulged. Boole had made this worry very explicit in his less known writings, but all of them tried to present the cold rational side of their thought as if to disown the romantic thread which guided them into the great mathematical developments of the nineteenth century. Perhaps I exaggerated this theme because it confirmed my thesis in this book that analogies, ratios and proportions provide the vital center of both poetry and mathematics. At any rate it made me write a small book, entitled *Symbolic Distance,* in which the bridge between the poetry of the trivium and the mathematics of the quadrivium was presented as a theory of measurement and fiction. It seemed to me that it would be through some such understanding that the modern liberal arts and sciences could bring the modern literatures and sciences into intelligible and teaching order.

When I returned from England, the battles of the liberal arts at Chicago and Virginia had grown to sieges and campaigns. At Chicago there were hardy recruits to the new investigation and construction that Adler was leading. At Virginia the Committee on Honors was enlarged. The emphasis at Chicago was on the subject matters of literature and the humanities, including philosophy. I decided that I would balance this emphasis by attending courses in mathematics and physics taught by friends who were sympathetic to my questions. We kept the two universities in communication by exchanging lecturers who dealt mainly with the technical doctrines of symbols in logic and in mathematics, a kind of counter-doctrine to the growing movements of semantics, logical positivism, and pragmatism.

By 1935 the Virginia Committee on Honors had argued itself to a unanimous report which went far beyond the original assignment. Instead of recommending special work for selected students in the last two undergraduate years of the college, we proposed that a curriculum be offered to a few students in their first two years. This curriculum would be based on a hundred great books, the original list for Columbia honors students reduced to half-length and supplemented by great books in science, Euclid, Ptolemy, Copernicus, Kepler, Galileo, Newton, Fourier, Clerk-Maxwell, and Claude

Bernard. There would be tutorials in languages and mathematics, and laboratories in which the great crucial experiments would be repeated. The central piece in the curriculum would be seminars for discussion of the great books themselves. We hoped that this recommendation would start a few students on their own self-education, and that the curriculum would finally be accepted by the whole college.

We had asked for what has later come to be called a pilot plant. It would take money to make it the model that would be imitated, $30,000 annually for thirty students, six instructors, and separate living and study arrangements. By this time President Alderman, who had originally appointed the Committee, had died, and Acting President Newcomb did not want to seem to overreach his temporary powers by undertaking such a radical departure from the conventional elective system in undergraduate education. The committee's recommendations were put on the shelf for lack of money.

The situation at Chicago was more favorable. President Hutchins, who had by this time published his book, *The Higher Learning in America,* had been able to raise enough money to establish a Committee on the Liberal Arts. Hutchins and Adler had led a seminar in the great books for some years. McKeon, as Dean of Humanities, could release some of the time of his colleagues and graduate students for the work of the Committee. Stringfellow Barr and I were invited to join and bring some of our graduate students with us.

The first meeting of the Committee on Liberal Arts will never be forgotten by any of those present. It was one of those occasions of recognition that mark the crises in tragedies and comedies as they are described in the last chapter of this book. Although there was good will and agreement on the problems set by poetry and mathematics, or the liberal arts, and in spite of many interchanges of lectures and papers, McKeon, Adler, and I, each of us, had constructed and complicated quite different universes of discourse which reached into deep matters of method and metaphysics. The three worlds separately had absorbed and accumulated the energies of our associates. They also carried within them the stresses and strains in our chaotic intellectual culture. Brought into proximity, the three worlds discharged their energies at each other. Heat and light became thunder and lightning. There was never another general meeting of the whole committee. We agreed to disagree and to pursue our separate courses.

Although there were sharp and clear intellectual differences that separated us, differences that cannot be expounded here, and also some differences that have always issued in what are traditionally known as "battles of the liberal arts," there were more practical difficulties in the strategy and organization of education that required separate working solutions or laboratories of experimentation. Hutchins, Adler, and McKeon had already introduced an educational ferment into the large University of Chicago. They had a strong following among the faculty and the students; also a strong opposition. They had obligations to continue. The Virginia contingent, as Barr and I and our associates called ourselves, had brought the Virginia plan which needed a more speculative development in an ivory tower before it could undertake the problem of practice and administration. This we did in the isolation of one of the stone towers at the University during the remainder of the year.

The rest of the story has been, since 1937, public knowledge of the time. Barr and I and our associates went to St. John's College in Annapolis, where the trustees allowed us to re-establish a very sick college according to the outlines of the Virginia plan. Hutchins, Adler, and McKeon and their associates continued to reorganize the college at the University of Chicago. Because of the general academic opposition to both, the differences between Chicago and St. John's and the developments they led to have never been clear to the public. Perhaps they do not need clarification, since the confusion in American education has increased.

Although the terms of the many-sided educational controversy of the 1960's are not clear, I hear in the battles of words echoes of the causes of the 'twenties and 'thirties. I even hear in C. P. Snow's report on the Two Cultures the continuing ballet of poetry and mathematics. The parts that they play in the technological integration of our time have still to be sorted out and appraised.

S. B.

Santa Barbara, Calif.
September 4, 1961

POETRY AND MATHEMATICS

1 ❧ POETRY AND MATHEMATICS

OUR IMMEDIATE INTELLECTUAL ANCESTORS were accustomed to speak of their neat and stuffy world as if it were an island of light in a sea of darkness. The figure of speech, together with the fact that they felt keenly what it expresses, conveys to us something of the origin of most of our predicaments. They were really describing a ghost, one of many which we have in our present intellectual twilight. We would rather speak, more literally, as we think, about the defects in our vision. We call our half-sight confusion, which I suppose means that we have many ghosts that we cannot tell apart.

Two of them who now walk most frequently, probably because of some peculiar odor rising from the witch's pot of industry and advertising, are inescapable for most people. They manifest a dignified agitation which is most contagious and upsetting. They seem to demand credulity and devotion, and when that is granted, run into the most whimsical and sometimes insane fits, exchanging and re-exchanging their disguises, and leaving their victims in hypnotic postures, or weak and disillusioned lethargies.

When they are entertained in the best society, they are known

ematics and poetry. That they are often so entertained is
of a long record of certified and revered activities. They
unded secret societies, they have revealed the truths of religion, they have trained physicians and magicians. Their more sober
and at present most respected occupations are engineering and demo-
cratic government. For a few they are always capped and gowned
educators and edifiers.

However much their appearances and activities may vary, they
are always found together, one of them talking while the other
works, and it is always difficult to find out whether it is the talk or
the work that produces the results. Sometimes it is quite clear that
the talk is in truth necessary to the work, but its value lies in its
irrelevance and prestidigitatory finesse. It is no wonder that we are
confused.

I am going to try to expose these ghosts. In the main I shall try
to do it by analysis and illustration that shall educe from the reader
an immediate realization of what they are. But before I proceed, I
think it will be well to introduce the characters by saying what they
are not, but are often supposed to be.

Mathematics suffers much, but most of all from its teachers. As a
result of bad pedagogy—and I mean the kind often judged best by
administrative pedagogues—the appearance of an algebraic formula,
a geometrical figure, or an innocent set of symbols reduces the reader
to an unbecoming attitude of hypocritical humility. A great many
sometime students of mathematics try to persuade themselves that
they haven't mathematical minds, when as a matter of fact they have
only had nonmathematical teachers. Mathematics is not what most
teachers of mathematics teach. They, with the good intention of con-
veying what they themselves have only as a skill of manipulation,
have unconsciously worked hocus-pocus on their pupils. They have
repeated and illustrated opaque formulae, sometimes to the admira-

tion, but almost always to the bewilderment, of their students. The honest-minded individual has in the end, however, been resilient and recovered from such maltreatment. The textbook makers and the psychologists of education have often found the ritual ineffective; on such occasions they have rearranged the words and introduced illustrations in what is known as the psychological order. The illustrations, precisely because they were already known, remained, as they were, "facts," and the formula that comes at the end remained also, as it always had been, a matter for summarizing memory, or "outside the scope of this book." Later the student, falling by chance into some mathematical mode of thought, is shocked to discover that he has been doing mathematics with his nonmathematical mind.

In general the teacher of mathematics has been the high priest of an occult ritual, the keeper in many senses of an esoteric doctrine which only his superiors or predecessors have understood. It is no wonder that Croce, the philosophical observer of a very fruitful period of Italian mathematics and education, should have given as his final dictum on mathematics that it is a mnemonic device, like Pelmanism, merely mimicking the intellectual activities of the human mind. He is rightly describing the exoteric student of mathematics, within which classification he himself falls.

Mathematics is not a compendium of memorizable formula and magically manipulated figures. Sometimes it uses formulae and manipulates figures, but it does this because it is concerned with ideas already familiar to the ordinary mind, but needing special sets of words or symbols for the sake of precise expression and efficient communication. Further, the abstraction thus signalized, which most people from bad emotional habits fear, is actually much more familiar to the untrained mind than any observed facts could possibly be. Abstract ideas are of the very tissue of the human mind. For this reason and for many others, illustration of mathematics by concrete event, fact, or object is never as effective as illustration by equally abstract analogous ideas. But here I am dangerously near giving away the secret of the title and we are not ready for it yet.

"Proof" is another word to conjure with. This word also has been spoiled by teachers of mathematics, but perhaps even more by the emphasis laid on the conventions of mathematical exposition by certain kinds of mathematical writers. It has come to be believed that the professional mathematician is a prover of propositions. From that belief it follows that mathematics is concerned with rigid structures, chains, and networks of propositions which are related as premises and conclusions of scholastic argument. For one who has not found it necessary to argue as a lawyer in a courtroom, this makes mathematics tedious and empty. It clips the wings of the human spirit.

For a philosopher perhaps this is the saddest of all the misconceptions of mathematics, for with it goes another misconception and hatred—that which is directed at logic and speculative thought in general. It is therefore easy and pleasant to criticize, even though many mathematicians will not agree.

It is true that mathematics sometimes deals with rigid structures, chains, and networks, but they are not made of propositions, and long and elaborate arguments are most often bad mathematics. The structures with which mathematics deals are more like lace, the leaves of trees, and the play of light and shadow on a meadow or a human face, than they are like buildings and machines, the least of their representatives. The best proofs in mathematics are short and crisp like epigrams, and the longest have swings and rhythms that are like music. The structures of mathematics and the propositions about them are ways for the imagination to travel and the wings, or legs, or vehicles to take you where you want to go. The solemn sound of demonstrated mathematical truths is a professional way of announcing an arrival at some point on the journey fantastic. Let it be added for good measure that some of the greatest mathematical discoveries by the greatest mathematical minds have been theorems that they could not prove; some have never been proved. The fact of the matter is that anything worth discovering in mathematics does not need proof; it needs only to be seen or understood. I hope this will become clear as I proceed. I also hope that the uses and relevance of proofs as aids to understanding and mathematical sight will appear in their proper places.

Symbols, formulae and proofs have another hypnotic effect. Because they are not immediately understood, they, like certain jokes, are suspected of holding in some sort of magic embrace the secret of the universe, or at least some of its more hidden parts. First, it may be noted that a few numbers or counters record the contents of a wallet or a treasure chest. They will also balance against debts owed by the owner. Further, by proper manipulation numbers on slips of paper produce the same practical effects as weighed units of gold or silver—they pay bills. Finally the man who sits at his desk and inscribes numbers and code messages on bits of paper controls the markets of the world. By faith in the checking code we move ourselves, our possessions, and finally mountains. The scientist tries a similar trick on what he sees and what he would like to see in the laboratory; he decodes nature and translates his and nature's secret into a formula. The doctor of occult science sees wisdom in all that the banker and physicist have recorded and stamps it with the seal of divine knowledge. Mathematics then becomes the ladder by which we all may climb into the heaven of perfect insight and eternal satisfaction, and the solution of arithmetic and algebraic problems is connected with the salvation of our souls.

The prestige of the engineer is another accretion to the tradition of mathematics. This more than any other one thing accounts for our present mathematical complex. The engineer is fast taking the position of authority, superseding the priest, the scholar, and the statesman in our organized thought and action. We ask and take his word, not only in practical matters where the question is how to do something, but also in theoretical matters where the question is what a thing is. Therefore, when the engineer says that his specialty is mathematics, we are doubly confident that his answer and practice are correct in this field.

Unfortunately the question, what is mathematics? is one question he has never asked. It is true he has learned to use it, especially those parts of it that deal with margins of safety and error, but like good workmen in other fields, his attention is on his skill and results rather than on his tools. Consequently his mathematics is intellectually patchy, a set of rules and facts good only for approximate measurement and plan-making. Like the computations in navigation it tells one more about sailing a ship than it does about the sun, moon, and stars. We shall find it difficult, if not impossible, to distinguish between applied mathematics and astrology, alchemy, and the occult arts. As these have fogged many minds in the past, so does the whole field of applied science based on mathematics today. It makes our industry possible and makes us worry about the future of our civilization. Watch the engineer and you will learn many things, but do not ask him about mathematics, unless you want to see quite another thing, how technology and folk-lore get invented and broadcast. A good part of the prestige of mathematics as a science is due to the contagion of such superstition. Let not your piety mislead your understanding.

Perhaps this is the place to introduce poetry, the other and perhaps better part of engineering. Every art has its mythology and ritual. So mathematics, when it becomes an art, fuses rhythmic language and gesture with intoxicating action and fact. The engineer sings as he works—often he only whistles—and in that singing there is the magic of poetry. The engineer's science, like the sailor's chanty, is good literature.

Professional poets are very often, more frequently than mathematicians, bad critics of themselves and their work. The wisest of them refuse to talk about poetry, leaving analysis and description to their more voluble companions, the critics. The critics, in turn, see so many different things reflected in poetry that they get confused and talk about many other things, among which poetry itself only incidentally gets attention. Thus it comes about that most of us only accidentally recognize poetry when we see it, and at the same time we follow the critics in using a verbal blunderbuss in our "literary conversations." The result is an intellectual confusion not only about poetry but also about many other things with which poetry is concerned.

Unfortunately, both the poet and the critic are right, the former in his silence, and the latter in his necessary loquacity. They show by their respective behaviors that they know that about which they do not talk. For poetry, at least that aspect of it about which I wish to talk, is an essential activity of human beings. It is essential in the sense that no matter what human beings may be doing they are at least poets; as in the case of so many arts, what distinguishes poetry as a fine art is an added and somewhat arbitrary differentiation. Therefore to talk about it is in a peculiar sense redundant, for talking is essentially a poetic activity, and when its subject is poetry, it is an attempt to make poetry devour and digest itself. One has the choice of refraining from such cannibalism and paying a tribute of silence, or of talking so fast and about so many things that the subject comes in of itself as a by-product.

I shall add then to the stream of words more or less poetic, choosing that part of poetry which is most often compared and contrasted with mathematics, hoping by treating poetry mathematically and mathematics poetically, to show the mutual reflections and common illuminations that they afford.

Poetry is one of the finer arts and therefore, like mathematics and the other higher studies, has specialized and refined techniques. It deals with selected language devices and aspires to the purity of form achieved only by music. It is an esoteric art. Let no one enter here who is ignorant of versification or prosody. Beware of profaning the sanctuary with sentimentality or flippant facilities. Discipline is the only road to achievement. This is the talk of the poetry workshop, the literary correlate of the Academy for painting and sculpture. It is the sage advice of professional and laureate poets. Unfortunately many great poets have not had the advantges of this higher education.

The answer comes from the poetry circle and the salon where poetry is read—with appreciation. Discriminating judgment is here scaled to the thermometer of inspiration. The poet is the seer of strange visions and polite purveyor of his insights to the vibrant few who have lived or desire to live and therefore understand. For the devotees the material of their enthusiasm is emotion recollected in intense tranquillity and released under properly controlled atmospheric conditions to drive the moral engines. Edification is the process induced and the ascent attains the plane of the higher life.

This aspect of poetry is an incident in the histories of religion and attests a character in poetry which is always subject to religious development. There are always those who will worship at the shrines of unknown gods, and it is not an unknown miracle that they often thus discover the god upon whom they wait.

Thus in the course of time the psychological critic is called in for consultation on the case. He first appears as Pan to prove the heretical nature of the poet and his cult. Then he uncovers the sins out of which the heresy grew. The worshipers justify the sins and absolve the sinner, whereupon the critic renames his victims after some fashionable neurosis, outlaws the poet, and at the same time encourages him to wander fancy-free in the Elysian fields of the abnormal. Inspiration is madness, and romance is release or compensation for early thwartings.

Psychoanalysis for art's sake is not a modern discovery. It has always been an adjunct to the temple, and the psychopathology of the poet is always a powerful, though sometimes a suppressed, interest of readers of poetry. The question, what does poetry express, is most satisfactorily answered in diagnostic and therapeutic terms. A more learned person than I might write a companion essay to this on Medicine and Poetry, laboriously making explicit the theory lying back of such collections of verse as are often called "The Poetry Cure" and "Heart Throbs," and at the same time indirectly commenting on the true subject matter of such books as *The Poetic Mind* and *The Road to Xanadu.*

Such exploitation of poetry for hygienic purposes cannot be condemned, but its quality as poetry, or poetic talk about poetry, can be noted and the naïveté of the school of psychological criticism made a matter of historical record.

The economist and sociologist will then find it and make their no less naïve case more compelling. The poet with his peculiar social heritage and delicately sensitive recording apparatus then becomes a member of the lowest rank of researchers, giving the first fumbling formulation of social conditions or *Zeitgeist.* But the poet has his revenge, for with the sociologist's reverence and hunger for recorded fact, the written word containing all the dream and madness of the writer has been accepted and gobbled up as historical evidence and is only rediscovered at some later time as the somewhat eerie and woolly conclusion of a social science. Inspiration has thus been transfigured into the spirit of the age or the progress of humanity.

The outcome of all this is the hard-headed conclusion of some scientific philosopher that poetry is not true. This for a hard head means that it is false. Since falsity is deception, and deception is immoral, and one ought to be moral, one must eschew poetry. The reasoning here is bad enough, but the poetry is good, at least, in its expression of human moral intent. The actual point made is a vigorous preference for one as against another kind of poetry, namely that which has a literal interpretive reference to personally collected fact. In this light, science becomes the most modern and authentic technique of poetry. The scientist is the contemporary monk copyist, writing over old literature on the palimpsest of experience, triumphantly announcing his faithfulness and accuracy in transferring the copy. *Hypotheses non fingo.* He only selects according to the canons of his school.

It will be noticed here that mathematics and poetry move together between two extremes of mysticism, the mysticism of the commonplace where ideas illuminate and create facts, and the mysticism of the extraordinary where God, the Infinite, the Real, poses the riddles of desire and disappointment, sin and salvation, effort and failure, question and paradoxical answer. It is commonly supposed that science and common sense avoid these mysteries and futilities. The tradition of experimental science has strengthened our confidence in the unaided senses and intellect. But latterly things and ideas in these regions have been behaving peculiarly. The ghosts so confidently laid by Francis Bacon and his followers are again walking in the laboratory as well as beside the man in the street. There is something persistent in what the whimsical and uncontrollable universe of ideas does to our experience, something with which Pythagoras, Plato, Plotinus, St. Augustine, Nicolas of Cusa, Galileo, Kant, and probably Einstein would be more familiar than the modern prophets who preach the control of nature. They would have called it by different names, each appropriate to the several historical occasions on which crises similar to our own have occurred. Some would have speculated about the foundations of the universe, some about the origin of the laws of nature, some about the Incarnation, some about the spontaneity of the human imagination, others about a possible transformation formula for Euclidean and non-Euclidean geometries.

Without intending to beg any metaphysical questions, I shall be referring to that sort of thing when I speak of poetry and mathematics and treating them as of equal importance and parallel developments in human culture. The nicest term to describe it is *logos,* which in Greek means equally "word" and "reason." I shall not burden the reader with further words of reverence for its historical dignity.

Very simply, poetry and mathematics are two very successful attempts to deal with ideas. In this respect they are genuine. Both employ sets of symbols and systems of notation. In this respect they have very interesting and illuminating comparisons and contrasts. As they revolve through their life cycles of fantasy, utility, culture, truth, and falsity, they reveal what I shall call aspects of the mathematical and poetic object. These accidental aspects merge and separate, giving their objects a very puzzling Protean character. They exchange disguises so that mathematics, commonly accepted for its hard-headedness, rigor and accuracy, is often poetry creating a realm of fancy; and poetry, commonly loved for its playful spontaneity and utter ineffectualness, becomes the mathematical demiurge joining words and images into a world of hard persuasive fact.

It is good fun, if not a task of paramount importance, to disentangle these aspects and trace their origins back to the mathematical and poetic objects—and thus learn to live with what are now ghosts behaving like somewhat mad Siamese twins.

The clarification of any idea, however simple or complex it may be, begins with its location on that translucent phosphorescent surface of man's thought that Plato called opinion or belief. Whether thought is like some distant gaseous star announcing its presence by a spot of light in the heavens, or like a witches' pot of potent herbs, fiery liquids and smelly vapors, boiling at the center of the human psyche, first examination always discloses this scum of amorphous cloudy opinion that represents and at the same time obscures the interior essences. The presumption is that everything inside sends up and out some ambiguous efflux of itself which is then held in suspension by the inner pressures and attractions. The astrophysicist makes telescopic and spectroscopic observations, and infers the nature of the inner fire and commotion. The psychoanalyst listens to words and watches gestures, and infers the chemistry of the soul. The dialectician by critical questioning intellectualizes and progressively eliminates the confusions of opinion until the idea stands clear and immediate to direct intuition.

Eddington and Freud are astrophysicist and psychoanalyst at present; Plato is the dialectician for all time. All three are good to mention in connection with the present undertaking, because they have been concerned, to be sure from different angles, with what I mean by poetry and mathematics. But Plato is especially relevant, not only because I too wish to be a dialectician, but also because he dealt most successfully with a crisis in the life of reason very similar to that which I wish to point out in the present.

The method and style of thought known as Pythagoreanism had achieved marked success in combining poetry and mathematics, and opinion among the Greeks showed all the vagaries and caricatures that one can imagine it possible to attach to the esoteric doctrine. Plato, the dialectician, had more than any other one man to do with the clarification of this opinion which finally issued in the science of Aristotle and the geometry of Euclid. Contemporary science shows the unmistakable symptoms of Pythagoreanism, and ordinary opinion and our rather extraordinary beliefs play with the vagaries and caricatures that are its typical companions.

Plato's method, as I have intimated, was to start with such opinion and by the continuous alternation of tentative hypothesis and criticism to make ever finer and more just distinctions until, in the language of the *Sophist,* the sameness and difference, the one and the many, the being and the non-being of the subject matter were obvious.

The literary style into which such philosophic criticism falls should be, as in Plato's model, the dialogue. Dialogue and dialectic show their affinities even in their names. But the dialogue is always a difficult form to construct, and at present it is a weak and patience-taxing vehicle of communication. Therefore, I propose to put this dialectical attempt into the less happy and adequate, but more economical, form of the essay.

By way of introducing the chief characters of the essay, I have referred them, poetry and mathematics, to the last pair of Plato's categories, their being and non-being, what they are and what they are supposed to be but are not. This ought to prepare the ground for the chapters immediately following which discuss their one and many aspects. The last two chapters deal more specifically with their similarities and differences.

To any popularizer of knowledge, let this be an invitation to suspend his labors of enlightenment until he has considered the following points in the analysis of his subject matter. I can assure him that the analysis has been made for the sake of his subject matter as much as in criticism of the aim and method of his treatment of it. His sin is usually called the inaccurate statement of half-truths. This is the burden of the criticism of all literature. Its opposing virtue, comprehensiveness and precision, is usually monopolized by the mathematician and is called *elegance*. He boasts of the economy of his style. But it is also an essential, though old-fashioned, virtue in literature. It usually requires a fundamental rethinking of a subject matter. I hope this essay will at least in an indirect way contribute to the wider achievement of this virtue.

2 ❦ FIGURES

EACH SYMBOL USED IN MATHEMATICS, whether it be a diagram, a numeral, a letter, a sign, or a conventional hieroglyph, may be understood as a vehicle which someone has used on a journey of discovery. Many have ridden all their lives on one or another set of these symbols without finding what they were looking for, namely, the meaning of the symbol. Sometimes the riding has been so enjoyable and fruitful in by-products that the original quest has been forgotten and the question has gone unanswered until some second rider has pushed on to the end. This is the extraordinary feature of mathematical study and perhaps one of the causes of bewilderment in its students. It gives perhaps a deeper meaning than is usually assigned to Euclid's famous remark that "there is no royal road to geometry."

However, as I have intimated in the preceding chapter, the vehicles are not mathematics, and too much attention can easily be given to unessentials. Fortunately it is the privilege of anyone at this period of history to forget the ride and the vehicles used and grasp immediately the discovered object of many of the journeys. At any rate, many of the roads can be telescoped or leaped over. Furthermore it is very important to do some of this reconnoitering at the beginning, in order to keep direction and thus maintain the proper proportion between effort and interest. This is true even for the professional mathematician. It is a necessity for the amateur. It may be added that the intuitive method is the basic procedure even for the rigorous step-by-step construction of elaborate mathematical systems.

Each journey then ends in some aspect of the mathematical object for which we search, and the next few chapters, beginning with this, will be telescoped flights from the bare symbol to some essential character of this object.

The first and perhaps the most illuminating question in mathematics is, what is a geometrical figure? I shall answer it in very general terms and then proceed to uncover their meanings. A figure in geometry is the sort of thing that retains an identical character throughout a series of possible transformations.

Lewis Carroll's Alice is obviously a geometrical figure on many occasions in Wonderland. In fact many of the characters in Lewis Carroll's writings conform to the preliminary definition I have given, and Lewis Carroll is not the only mathematician who has been able to present the mathematical object in alternative languages.

The Caterpillar in Chapter V of *Alice in Wonderland* is a typical teacher of mathematics, and Alice is a typical pupil, in this case doubly surprised and bewildered because she is at the same time the figure to be understood. Incidentally, she was also learning some first lessons in modern relativity.

> The Caterpillar and Alice looked at each other for some time in silence: at last the Caterpillar took the hookah out of its mouth, and addressed her in a languid, sleepy voice.
> "Who are *you?*" said the Caterpillar.
> This was not an encouraging opening for a conversation. Alice replied, rather shyly, "I—I hardly know, sir, just at present—at least I know who I *was* when I got up this morning, but I think I must have been changed several times since then."

"What do you mean by that?" said the Caterpillar sternly. "Explain yourself!"

"I can't explain *myself*, I'm afraid, sir," said Alice, "because I'm not myself, you see."

"I don't see," said the Caterpillar.

"I'm afraid I can't put it more clearly," Alice replied very politely, "for I can't understand it myself, to begin with; and being so many different sizes in a day is very confusing."

"It isn't," said the Caterpillar.

"Well, perhaps you haven't found it so yet," said Alice, "but when you have to turn into a chrysalis—you will some day, you know—and then after that into a butterfly, I should think you'll feel it a little queer, won't you?"

"Not a bit," said the Caterpillar.

"Well, perhaps *your* feelings may be different," said Alice; "all I know is, it would feel very queer to *me*."

"You!" said the Caterpillar contemptuously. "Who are *you?*"

Which brought them back again to the beginning of the conversation. Alice felt a little irritated at the Caterpillar's making such *very* short remarks, and she drew herself up and said very gravely, "I think you ought to tell me who *you* are, first."

"Why?" said the Caterpillar.

Here was another puzzling question; and as Alice could not think of any good reason, and as the Caterpillar seemed to be in a *very* unpleasant state of mind, she turned away.

"Come back!" the Caterpillar called after her. "I've something important to say!"

This sounded promising, certainly. Alice turned and came back again.

"Keep your temper," said the Caterpillar.

"Is that all?" said Alice, swallowing down her anger as well as she could.

"No," said the Caterpillar.

Alice thought she might as well wait, as she had nothing else to do, and perhaps after all it might tell her something worth hearing. For some minutes it puffed away without speaking; but at last it unfolded its arms, took the hookah out of its mouth again, and said, "So you think you're changed, do you?"

"I'm afraid I am, sir," said Alice; "I can't remember things as I used—and I don't keep the same size for ten minutes together!"

"Can't remember *what* things?" said the Caterpillar.

"Well, I've tried to say 'How doth the little busy bee,' but it all came different!" Alice replied in a very melancholy voice.

"Repeat 'You are old, Father William,' " said the Caterpillar.

Alice folded her hands, and began:

" 'You are old, Father William,' the young man said,
    'And your hair has become very white,
   And yet you incessantly stand on your head—
    Do you think, at your age, it is right?' "

. . . .

"That is not said right," said the Caterpillar.

"Not *quite* right, I'm afraid," said Alice timidly; "some of the words have got altered."

"It is wrong from beginning to end," said the Caterpillar decidedly, and there was silence for some minutes.

The Caterpillar was the first to speak.

"What size do you want to be?" it asked.

"Oh, I'm not particular as to size," Alice hastily replied; "only one doesn't like changing so often, you know."

"I *don't* know," said the Caterpillar.

Alice said nothing; she had never been so much contradicted in all her life before, and she felt that she was losing her temper.

"Are you content now?" said the Caterpillar.

"Well, I should like to be a *little* larger, sir, if you wouldn't mind," said Alice; "three inches is such a wretched height to be."

"It is a very good height indeed!" said the Caterpillar angrily, rearing itself upright as it spoke (it was exactly three inches high).

"But I'm not used to it!" pleaded poor Alice in a piteous tone. And she thought to herself, "I wish the creature wouldn't be so easily offended!"

"You'll get used to it in time," said the Caterpillar, and it put the hookah into its mouth and began smoking again.

This time Alice waited patiently until it chose to speak again. In a minute or two the Caterpillar took the hookah out of its mouth, and yawned once or twice, and shook itself. Then it got down off the mushroom, and crawled away into the grass, merely remarking as it went, "One side will make you grow taller, and the other side will make you grow shorter."

"One side of *what*? The other side of *what*?" thought Alice to herself.

"Of the mushroom," said the Caterpillar, just as if she had asked it aloud; and in another moment it was out of sight.

Alice remained looking thoughtfully at the mushroom for a minute, trying to make out which were the two sides of it; and, as it was perfectly round, she found this a very difficult question. However, at last she stretched her arms round it as far as they would go, and broke off a bit of the edge with each hand.

"And now which is which?" she said to herself, and nibbled a little of the right-hand bit to try the effect: the next moment she felt a violent blow underneath her chin; it had struck her foot.

She was a good deal frightened by this very sudden change, but she felt that there was no time to be lost, as she was shrinking rapidly; so she set to work at once to eat some of the other bit. Her chin was pressed so closely against her foot that there was hardly room to open her mouth; but she did it at last, and managed to swallow a morsel of the left-hand bit. . . .

"Come, my head's free at last!" said Alice in a tone of delight, which changed into alarm in another moment, when she found that her shoulders were nowhere to be found; all she could see, when she looked down, was an immense length of neck, which seemed to rise like a stalk out of a sea of green leaves that lay far below her.

"What *can* all that green stuff be?" said Alice. "And where *have* my shoulders got to? And oh, my poor hands, how is it I can't see you?" She was moving them about as she spoke, but no result seemed to follow, except a little shaking among the distant green leaves.

As there seemed to be no chance of getting her hands up to her head, she tried to get her head down to them, and was delighted to find that her neck would bend about easily in any direction, like a serpent. She had just succeeded in curving it down into a graceful zigzag, and was going to dive in among the leaves, which she found to be nothing but the tops of the trees under which she had been wandering, when a sharp hiss made her draw back in a hurry; a large pigeon had flown into her face, and was beating her violently with its wings.

. . . .

Alice crouched down among the trees as well as she could, for her neck kept getting entangled among the branches, and every now and then she had to stop and untwist it. After a while she remembered that she still had the pieces of mushroom in her hands, and she set to work very carefully, nibbling first at one and then at the other, growing sometimes taller and sometimes shorter, until she had succeeded in bringing herself down to her usual height.

It was so long since she had been anything near the right size, that it felt quite strange at first, but she got used to it in a few minutes, and began talking to herself as usual. "Come, there's half my plan done now! I'm never sure what I'm going to be, from one minute to another! However, I've got back to my right size; the next thing is to get into that beautiful garden—how *is* that to be done, I wonder?" As she said this she came suddenly upon an open place, with a little house in it about four feet high. "Whoever lives there," thought Alice, "it'll never do to come upon them *this* size; why, I should frighten them out of their wits!" So she began nibbling at the right hand bit again, and did not venture to go near the house till she had brought herself down to nine inches high.

This is a highly generalized form of geometry. It is often called positional or projective geometry. Another case of it will be demanded by the conventional mathematician; I take the suggestion for it from an early work of Euclid on optics.

Suppose you are looking at some ordinary object, say a cup and saucer or a tree, and you begin speculating on the rays of light which are passing somehow from the many points of the cup and saucer or the tree. They are said to converge at some point of your eye, say between the lens and the retina. They pass through a common point. Now travel back along the bundle of rays. Stop at any point and pass a plane perpendicular to your line of vision so that it will cut all the rays from the object. You will then have on the plane a two-dimensional picture of the object. Each point in the visible object will have a corresponding point on the plane of projection. As you move the plane nearer you, you have a smaller picture, and as you move it toward the object, you have a larger picture. You will indeed have a series of possible pictures each corresponding to some possible position of the plane.

Suppose you move the plane away from you through the object, extending the rays as far as the plane. Move the plane ten feet back from the object, then one mile, then a thousand miles, as far as you please. The picture increases by definite degrees of magnification to any size you please. Bring the plane back to your eye, through the point of convergence where the picture seems to disappear in one point, and back through your head indefinitely. The picture again grows and, in a manner of speaking, grows infinitely large.

You have here a beautifully simple case of conic sections. For if you simplify the object to a sphere or a disc held perpendicular to your line of vision, the planes of projection in their various positions cut a cone of light rays whose apex is in your eye. Each section will be a circle. Change the angle of the plane to your line of vision and you can get ellipses, parabolas, and hyperbolas of any size. Each is a geometrical figure which has a long story about it in the history of mathematics. Around each of the operations with the cutting plane and the cone there has grown up a branch of mathematical study.

Projective geometry is interested in the transformations themselves: how a figure retains certain properties such as proportionality of lines and angles throughout given transformations; whether following a given set of these transformations will reproduce a given figure or always produce new ones; and the most general laws governing such properties.

Certain of these laws taken together will give you metric geometry. The application of these laws determines rigid lines and angles and these figures so produced have certain properties with which most students become familiar in courses on plane and solid geometry. It is geometry of this sort that has often clipped the wings of a young mathematical imagination. Metric geometry appears so obviously applicable that the intrinsic properties of its objects lose their charm and one becomes an inventor or engineer, and geometrical thought gets its first suppression. Then too, rigidity of line and angle has a mechanical aspect that at once frightens and hypnotizes the uninitiated into a frozen stare at what seem prison bars and mazes. This is one of the occasions when the two ghosts, mathematics and poetry, have contrived to be especially diabolical. The teacher of mathematics has introduced a bugaboo with regrettable results both in understanding and in discipline.

Rigidity is really there, but how different it is from its reputed character! The rigid figures of metric geometry are like the points of rest in the path of Zeno's famous arrow. They are the arbitrary termini of intervals, paradoxical if taken by themselves, but intelligible enough if understood as stages in a projective development or as materials to be transformed.

We have tried the variations in a single conic projective field. We accomplished that development by shifting a projective plane. Suppose now we hold the plane fixed and shift the apex of the cone. We are looking at a circle. When the line of vision is perpendicular to the plane of the circle, we see a circle. Moving away from the plane in the same line of vision makes the circle grow smaller. This shows the simple principle of painter's perspective. Now suppose we begin to move around the circle. We see a series of ellipses each a little flatter than the preceding one until, when our line of vision is in the plane of the circle, the ellipse becomes a straight line indistinguishable in length and position from the vertical diameter of the circle. Continuing our revolution around the circle, we again see the ellipses becoming fatter and finally achieving circularity. Varying the orbit of our point of vision, we can travel ideally to any point in space, and for each station on the way there will be a corresponding geometric figure discernible. Certain philosophers have proposed this set of figures as a solution of the problem of perception in the theory of knowledge. A coin is the series of aspects possible to realize by this method in all the points of space. These philosophers have been hypnotized by a field of projection whose "rigidity" they have taken for substance. But they are right about the "rigidity" of these fields of projection. Although it would take a super-aviator, a very whimsical old lady on a broom, a disembodied fairy, or a relativity physicist to realize even a small part of the field of projection of any given object, the conditions of the transformations, the sequence of the "aspects" and the relations between the aspects would follow a rule or principle of the sort which mathematicians and some philosophers would call eternal truths; they mean that something very much like the soul of the projective field remains constant throughout an indefinite number of variations. This field is itself a geometric figure and each variation is again such a figure. Mathematical philosophers whose imaginations are touched with poetry, such as Leibniz and Bruno, see in this an account of the whole universe. It is constituted of points or monads each mirroring the whole. In other words, the universe is a very complex but unified projective field constituted of projective fields. But Leibniz, at any rate, saw that such a universe was not material; its rigidity was not a physical rigidity. Its rigidity is the rigidity of a speculative imagination.

It is not difficult to see how this sort of rigor is invoked by the poet along with the inspiration of his particular muse. Even a short poem that gives words to a mood discovers and reveals a structure, at once simple and very complex. It makes very little difference whether it is a means to the end of communicating an emotion or whether it is the very final end of the creative activity; it comes with the inspiration of the muse, and is negligible only because it will be there even when not explicitly invited.

Also even in a short poem, this structure undergoes transformation. The poet may select only the crucial changes and never note the principle, but if the poem is successful it records the intellectual rhythm along with the verbal choreography. In longer poems and in semipoetic literature, such as the drama and the novel, there is always an element, often called character, leitmotiv, or idea, undergoing a development. Amid this change, it stands or becomes increasingly rigid and, for some readers and writers, substantial and real. The development may be a temporal affair, like a life or series of incidents, or it may be merely the process of revelation and clarification in the writing, but it is development by transformation in both cases. This variation according to rule is what Aristotle meant by "action" in the *Poetics*. "Poetry is the imitation of an action," the generation of a form, the adumbration of an essence. I think the comparison of mathematics and poetry is illuminating on this point, for this is one of the places where a poem and a geometrical demonstration meet. A demonstration, as we shall see, uncovers a figure in transformation just as a poem reveals a character in action. The demonstration tries to be literal; this quality is sometimes called accuracy and exactness. The poem tries to be adequate; its quality is sometimes called imagination and associative eloquence. I shall not ask the question here how far each succeeds.

The mathematical technique will clarify both. The triangle is an obsession to geometers and the rest of the world may be grateful to the geometer for cultivating such a neurosis. For most of the successful solutions of problems have been due to knowledge of triangles and their application in triangulation. It has been suggested that the Greeks had an overdeveloped Oedipus complex issuing in a fixation on the eternal triangle, and the rationalization of it ended in Euclid's *Elements*. Literary critics of the psychological school do not like this exploitation of their methods, but they should know the abundance of evidence for such an hypothesis. It is what they would call overwhelming. Plato has collected much of the evidence from the Pythagorean writings and the *Timaeus* is his account of the paranoid mechanisms of defense. It is there said that the world is constructed of triangular atoms, the chief of which is an earth atom—poor Mother Earth and the Oedipean Greeks!

Be that as it may, triangles are truly wonderful, and have enough poetry of their own without the adulteration provided by the psy-chologist. Chief among their various kinds is the right triangle and the most important knowledge we have of it is contained in the Py-thagorean theorem. It will serve many purposes of this chapter to recount the demonstration of this theorem with enough said about triangles in general to make that possible. Not least of these purposes is a certain piety due to the geometrical tradition.

Let us start then with some preliminary play with the triangle in general. Take a straight line of a given length as a base and from one end draw another line of any length you please. Leave it attached to the base line at one end and bring it down to a position that will leave a very small angle between. Connect the two free ends by a third line. You now have a very acute-angled triangle. Now swing the second line so as to increase the acute angle and allow the third line to expand and change its direction in any way so as to keep the triangle closed. By steadily increasing the angle between the base and second line, the triangle will undergo successive transformations, revealing one after another the precious properties of the triangle. For instance, by a moment's reflection, you will realize that by certain stipulations about the length of the base and second line and the angle between them, you will be determining the size of all the other lines and angles in the triangle. Similarly, if you fix the length of the base as we have done, and in addition the size of the angles at either end of it, you will have fixed the size of the other parts of the tri-angle. This property is usually recorded in textbooks by two theorems about the equality of triangles. From our point of view they are im-portant properties of the triangle in general.

Now continue the revolution of the second line until you have a right angle between it and the base line. This is a right triangle whose properties we are looking for. But before we go into that, let us find some more peculiarities of the general triangle. Continue the revolution of the second line and you have a series of obtuse triangles corresponding to stations of the second line in its revolution. It will be noticed that as the angle increases between the base line and the second line, the angle at the other end of the base line and the angle at the third vertex decrease in size. This kind of covariation is the sort of thing that a statistician thinks very significant. He would doubtless make a table of correlation in this case. We can accept what he says and go on to a further observation, namely, that as the second line continues to revolve and approach the direction of the base line, the other angles tend to disappear, and as it becomes an extension of the base line, the triangle disappears. The geometer here would be tempted to make a guess. He would reverse the revolution of the second line to some direction where it made a triangle possible. He would then draw a line from the vertex of revolution parallel to the third side of the triangle. He would also extend the base through the vertex. There would then be three angles at the vertex, one interior to the triangle and two exterior to it. Now by revolution of the second line, and by allowing the parallel to the third side to revolve so as to remain parallel, he would note the similarity of the changes in the two exterior angles and the opposite interior angles. They seem to remain equal, the opposite interior base angle to the exterior angle on the base, and the interior angle at the top vertex to the exterior angle on the second line. This is a clue worth following.

Upon investigation of parallel lines with lines running through them, it is found that the situation in our triangle exactly fulfills the conditions for two cases when the angles involved are always equal. In general, $x = w = a = d$, and $y = z = b = c$. Upon this discovery, it is easy to jump to a conclusion about the sum of the interior angles of any triangle. Their sum is always constant and equal to all the angles that can be drawn on one side of a line at a given point, or one hundred and eighty degrees. This then is a necessary condition of being a plane Euclidean triangle, one of those intangible rigidities with which geometry deals.

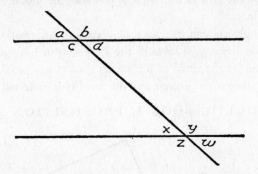

But the same figure is interesting for another reason. Draw a line from the top vertex parallel to the base letting it cut the parallel to the third line. We now have a parallelogram which is twice the original triangle. If you wish to convince yourself of this, apply the

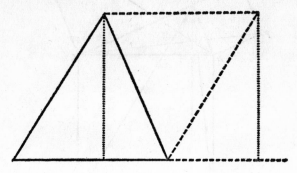

test for equal triangles and see that the second triangle is equal to the first. This may be stated formally in the theorem that the area of a parallelogram is equal to twice the area of one of the triangles formed by its diagonal. Further we can see that this area is the same as a rectangle having an equal base and altitude (the distance between the parallels along a perpendicular). Draw the altitude and see for yourself. So the area of a triangle is one half the product of its base and altitude.

Surprisingly enough, we have here enough information to allow us to put on the august robes of the Pythagorean initiate and enter the sanctum for the ritual of a rigorous geometrical proof. Here follows the Pythagorean theorem and the proof of it preferred by Euclid.

EUCLID, BOOK I, PROPOSITION 47

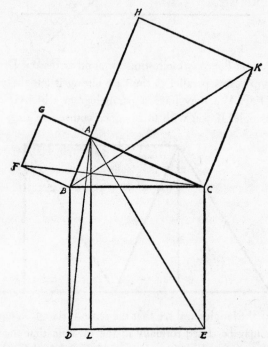

In right-angled triangles the square on the side subtending the right angle is equal to the squares on the sides containing the right angle.

Let ABC be a right-angled triangle having the angle BAC right; I say that the square on BC is equal to the squares on BA, AC.

For let there be described on BC the square BDEC, and on the BA, AC the squares GB, HC; through A let AL be drawn parallel to either BD or CE, and let AD, FC be joined.

Then, since each of the angles BAC, BAG is right, it follows that with a straight line BA, and at the point A on it, the two straight lines AC, AG not lying on the same side make adjacent angles equal to two right angles; therefore CA is in a straight line with AG.

For the same reason BA is also in a straight line with AH.

And, since the angle DBC is equal to the angle FBA: for each is right: let the angle ABC be added to each; therefore the whole angle DBA is equal to the whole angle FBC.

And, since DB is equal to BC, and FB to BA, the two sides AB, BD are equal to the two sides FB, BC respectively; and the angle ABD is equal to the angle FBC; therefore the base AD is equal to the base FC, and the triangle ABD is equal to the triangle FBC.

Now the parallelogram BL is double of the triangle ABD, for they have the same base BD and are in the same parallels BD, AL.

And the square GB is double of the triangle FBC, for they again have the same base FB and are in the same parallels FB, GC.

(But the doubles of equals are equal to one another.)

Therefore the parallelogram BL is also equal to the square GB.

Similarly if AE, BK be joined, the parallelogram CL can also be proved equal to the square HC; therefore the whole square BDEC is equal to the two squares GB, HC.

And the square BDEC is described on BC, and the squares GB, HC on BA, AC.

Therefore the square on the side BC is equal to the squares on the sides BA, AC.

Therefore in right-angled triangles the square on the side subtending the right angle is equal to the squares on the sides containing the right angle.

Quod erat demonstrandum.

This balances the quotation from Lewis Carroll above. There we become acquainted with Alice in a most intimate and exact way, and can easily understand the rest of Wonderland. Here we become familiar with the essence of the right triangle, and will have no difficulty in going on to trigonometry, navigation, surveying, and astronomy, in short, to the triangulation of the universe from atoms to stars. In both cases an abstract idea has been presented, defined, and clarified; so it is with the geometrical and poetical treatment of ideas in general. The subtleties of geometry and imaginative literature are all of this sort, intangible but intelligible things undergoing significant variation and finding themselves in the process.

Geometry has here been introduced without the usual emphasis on demonstration or proof. This has been intentional, but an apology to pedagogical geometry will not be out of place; it will serve two purposes. First, it will distinguish the essentials from the nonessentials of geometry, as it is taught; second, it will again make explicit the relation between mathematics and poetry.

It is said that the function of geometry is to prove propositions, and by proof, it is often claimed, it establishes the truth of what it says. The thought process involved is called deduction, and by this process it is supposed we infer from the truth of first principles or axioms, which are self-evidently true, the truth of everything that follows from them, including the proposition under discussion. This would undoubtedly be a good employment of geometrical thinking if it were ever possible to be sure of the first principles. Unfortunately, we never have such certainty, as has become increasingly evident since the discovery of non-Euclidean geometries which base themselves on axioms, or postulates as they are now called, which are not compatible with Euclid's assumptions. The truth of axioms is no more evident than the truth of any other propositions in geometry, and axioms hold preferred positions only in minds that can think of no alternatives.

It further appears that deduction is only one way of linking together mathematical insights that are acquired by nondeductive means, and that any one of these insights is as good as any other, provided it is actually seen intellectually. Deduction then becomes a secondary process, systematic and integrative for separate but prior intuitions, leading to and uncovering some unsuspected aspect of the mathematical object, or aiding in the fusing of separate parts of what finally becomes a geometric system. Thus the proof of the Pythagorean theorem brings together the subject matter of the first forty-six theorems of Euclid in one grand vision of geometric relations. The recent advance of Einstein in mathematical physics is a similar integration involving non-Euclidean systems of geometry and also insights which have previously been considered physical and nongeometrical.

Demonstration is a far better term to apply to the process, especially when it is taken to mean "a pointing out" of its subject matter. It then becomes the vehicle by which we travel over the mathematical territory and gain vantage points for seeing this or that field of connections.

The truth which is claimed for mathematics is the truth of clear vision where ideas are concerned. It is related to the truth of poetic vision by a close similarity. A poem is also the vehicle for the survey of an ideal territory and its destination is equally an integration of separate insights. All good demonstration should end in the unambiguous definition of its object; and each good poem can be seen as a definitive presentation of some poetic object.

But mathematical and poetic objects are subject to other treatments and manifest themselves in other guises. For instance, the transformations of geometry occur according to definite rules which determine the order of the elements. This order, which has been taken for granted in this chapter, is the subject of a special mathematical science, the science of numbers. It is the purpose of the next chapter to present this phase of mathematical and poetic thought.

3 ❦ NUMBERS

THERE IS NO MORE IMPRESSIVE FORM of literature than the narrative epic poem. That combination of depth and breadth of conception which some have called sublimity has here found a natural and adequate expression. The theory of number is the epic poem of mathematics. The mutual reflection of the two arts will supply a sort of explanation in the intellectual dimension of the epic quality in both. It will also show how it is that the number has made some of the discoveries in physical science possible; it is to be remarked that these physical discoveries themselves have an epic quality probably due to the part numbers have played in their technical development.

But the question, what is a number? is an invitation to analyze counting and to find out what sort of thing makes counting possible. In poetry I suppose the corresponding question would be, what makes recounting possible? The answer, if it were to be complete, would take us into the most abstract and subtle mathematical thought. But the key to the problem is the simplest sort of insight. The same peculiar combination of simplicity and subtlety is involved in the theory of narrative, but as everyone knows, insight here belongs to the most common of common-sense conceptions.

Very briefly, a number is an element in a field of variation. Its specific numerical property consists in its relations with other elements in the same field, which relations are expressed in rules of order. One can see immediately how a significant event or incident in a story conforms to this definition in the general form I have given it. In geometry, the emphasis is on the constancy of elements that undergo transformation; the emphasis in arithmetic is on the order and connection of the elements in the transformation itself. Arithmetic adds the "how" to geometry's "what." Numbers reveal another aspect of the mathematical object.

The structures that make counting possible are chains and networks of relations. The understanding of a selected few of these relations will be the suggestive key to the whole realm. There are two ways of approaching these relations. One has the advantage of being itself a kind of narrative that gathers up the main turning points in the history of arithmetic. This is the theory of operations. The other is postulate theory in which collections of elements are assumed and one relation after another is introduced until a mere aggregate becomes as if by magic a number system. I shall begin with the theory of operations. It is merely a careful account of counting with special attention paid to the difficulties met and solved or circumvented.

A point of beginning is assumed, usually the number one. This is the fulcrum demanded by Archimedes when he said he would move the world by means of levers. An operator, so called, is also taken—one of Archimedes' levers. This operator is called $+1$. Then there follows a rapid process of intellectual knitting starting with $1 + 1 = 2$, $2 + 1 = 3$, $3 + 1 = 4$, . . . and ending (?) with $n + 1$, and you have the series of positive numbers to infinity. Of course infinity is not a number in this series but "to infinity" describes a property of the series, namely, that it has only the arbitrary end you wish to assign it if you want a finite series; or it has no end, that is, no last term.

Then you take another operator, —1, and starting with any one of the positive numbers, you can travel backwards along this series until you arrive at 1. Here you encounter a difficulty, the solution of which once bothered the mathematical consciences of many men, as much as warped space does now. What can $1 - 1$ mean? The answer is another symbol, unknown before, and, in a sense, unknown still. It is one of those vehicles which one can ride without looking under the hood. Of course we know it is o. Once you learn to ride, it is easy enough. But still other vehicles had to be discovered or invented. For what does $0 - 1$ mean? Again consciences strained over answers obvious to us. Of course, —1. Then by more rapid knitting, another infinite series of negative numbers became known.

But this is not the end of the chain stitch. The operator $(\times)$ or $(\cdot)$ was applied and rapid jumps were made back and forth over the two series which were now combined into one, containing both positive and negative numbers. $3 \times 4 = 12$, $-3 \times +4 = -12$, and $-3 \times -4 = 12$. For every multiplicative combination of numbers, whether positive or negative, there is some corresponding number of the original series. Of course this is generalized to cover 1 and o by special convention and it is also true for additive and sub-tractive combinations.

By this time the mathematical conscience had taken on great versatility and inventiveness. The moral conscience has had similar awakenings, but more regressions to somnolence. Another operator was taken up with most amazing results. $12 \div 4$ is an easy jump, apparently the converse of 3×4, but what can $12 \div 5$ mean? If you answer $2\frac{2}{5}$, you have accepted a new convention with most revolutionary consequences. For then you can also write $\frac{2}{5}$ alone, meaning $2 \div 5$, and nothing more can be done about it. It just stands there immovable and indissoluble, unless you put it with another rather improper fraction, and $\frac{2}{5} \times \frac{5}{2} = 1$ or $\frac{2}{5} \times 5 = 2$. This however undermines all you have admitted before. 5 and 2 are really no different from $\frac{5}{1}$ and $\frac{2}{1}$, and the original series is only a few selected numbers from a still "more infinite" series of fractional numbers. This series is profoundly different from the first. For between any two numbers in it, it is possible to find a third, no matter how many you have introduced in that way before. It has no beginning and no end, and in a peculiar way Zeno's paradox about passing over an infinite number of points in finite time is given further exemplification even without points and time. You can never pass from one number to another by any thoroughly step-by-step procedure. It is now a riddle not only how bodies move, but also a much worse one, how anybody counts. Incidentally, in showing how we count, we have shown how counting is impossible.

It would seem that the people with mathematical consciences were wise in sticking to the positive integers and that these riders of newfangled vehicles have gone too far. On another occasion very much like this Bishop Berkeley accused mathematicians of dealing in symbols more vicious and unintelligible than those of theology, and others went on to show that if mathematicians could prove eternal truths by such obviously questionable methods, how much more right had mystics and preachers to use questionable arguments for which they made no such ambitious claims.

Obviously here is a tangle, but it is easy to unravel. Counting is not covering ground, any more than measuring a distance or telling a story is covering ground. It is a little more subtle. Counting has always to do with at least two sets of numbers, what have been called the numbering numbers and the numbered numbers, and the process is called one-oneing or correlation, that is, finding in one of two series a corresponding number for each number in the other. It is very easy to find a series of numbered numbers for the series of fractional or rational numbers. Euclidean space is such a series and in addition contains some extra numbers called irrationals. I shall have more to say about those when we come to the puzzles in the infinitesimal calculus. It is enough here to remark that the paradox of counting by means of an infinite series is only the occasion for new discoveries about the network of numbers. Operations merely outran analysis for a time, but like the tortoise, analysis catches up, and when it does, one sees that the conditions of the whole race are revised. Counting is a different thing because mathematicians played with unintelligible operations for a time.

But we must shift our ground of explanation of numbers to see just what this amounts to. The shift is like a certain one in narrative literature that happened long ago. At some time or other, it was supposed that a story was only a story. This has repeatedly returned as a very sophisticated dogma of criticism. Novelists are just story-tellers; to claim more for them is moralism, sociologism, psychologism, or something worse, intellectualism. But at some time between this revival and its previous vogue the story was more than a story. It bore a burden, sometimes an insight, and sometimes even a moral. Epic literature has often become sacred scripture and, even more often, the repository of a people's history and civilization. When it has done this, it has not been merely a record of events and gossip about them. It has been interpretive, as we used to say. It has had a certain generality or universality, to use a higher-sounding name. In still older lingo, it had a touch of eternity about it, transcending the flow of human affairs. Its people were heroes and often were mistaken for gods. All this may have been a mistake—certainly it has worked woe as well as weal for human affairs—but the fact remains that there is something in any good story which is capable of this exploitation. I suggest that that something is the relations holding between the events or incidents. In other words, the plot of a story is an intellectual as well as an aesthetic pattern and it is this that gives the incidental elements that float in it a significance. These patterns are very abstract, very general, and capable of infinite variation, so that they may be revised and re-applied without violating their essential forms. The speculative historian can attach them to a period and name them the form spirit—Magian, Apollian, or Faustian—but they are actually more general and if they must be attached, are more discriminating. The Cinderella story is in most primitive folklore, is exploited in the cult of mariolatry, and is now in the current American magazine story, just as it is the pattern running like a phrase of music in the head of the tired stenographer or shopgirl. Is it a story, or is it a meta-physic of morals?

I prefer to compare it with number, that age-old story recounted at one time on fingers and toes, at another in the knots of a rug, at another in the constellations, the letters of the alphabet, the beads of wampum, and the modern cash register of a ten-cent store. The affinity of stories and numbers is always latent, bursting forth in magic formulae, sacred numbers, astrology, alchemy, the Cabala, and the wisdom of the Rosicrucians, and periodically hypostasized into the supreme dogma of a universal religion, as in the Trinity or the infinitude of deities in Eastern religions. Numbers are not just counters; they are elements in a system. It is this aspect of numbers with which the story of postulate theory concerns itself. It is in the findings of such studies that the necessary conditions of counting are stated.

These results have come from a peculiar sort of study. The modern mathematician has been sitting down like an Epicurean god, far from space and time, calling for chaos to play with. He gives a few brief orders and watches universes grow. He varies the orders and universes give place to still others. Sometimes he creates one very much like that in which we are accustomed to think we live, and sometimes they are unusual and bizarre like a universe that we may become accustomed to living in if we change our minds. Sometimes a system comes out of such play that sets an old system in a new light. Such is the work on number postulates.

The technique is to assume entities, elements, what-not and carefully assign certain relations to hold between them. In the case of numbers, the relations are first left unnamed and unspecified except for very general properties usually called irreflexive, asymmetric, and transitive. A relation is irreflexive when it does not hold between identical terms. For instance, an ordinal number cannot be to the right of itself; "to the right of" is an irreflexive relation, where "same as" is reflexive. A relation is asymmetric when it holds only one way between two terms; an ordinal number cannot be to the right of another given number and yet have that number to the right of itself. "Same as" would also be symmetric. A transitive relation is one that allows the inference: if A is to the right of B, and B is to the right of C, then A is to the right of C. "To the right of" is transitive. Any relation that satisfies these three requirements can be made the generating relation for what is known as a progression, variations and restrictions of which lead to the various kinds of series which we call ordinal numbers. Some of these numbers are discrete, where each number has a next successor as in the series of whole numbers. Some are not discrete but compact, when no number has a next successor as in the series of fractions. Finally there are continuous series where, in addition to compactness, it is possible to discover numbers between those in the series of fractions, the so-called irrationals. There are still other numbers which are combinations of those previously described, curious results of operations of taking the square or even-numbered roots of -1. These are called imaginary numbers and belong in series. The subtleties of these conceptions can be reduced to the obvious simplicities of the properties of relations and the order they bring to a set of entities. This holds for ordinal numbers.

The account of cardinal numbers is a subject of some controversy, but the issue can also be reduced to simple enough notions. There are two ways of introducing the persons of a story. In one of these, a person is allowed to recall his past and thus reveal what sort of person he is, or his history is told in a casual way by another character or by the author. Sometimes court procedure is followed; a collection of opinions is entered from certified witnesses and the reader is allowed to act as jury to make a summary decision. The characters of the witnesses have to be known in some stereotyped manner to make this method effective. Around these two methods there are many possible variations, but the secret is the same as the secret of ordinal numbers. Each character is to be known by the external relations it has with other members of an array of similar or relevant characters. Fielding's Tom Jones is an example of such a character.

The other method leads to cardinal characters and numbers. The identity or individuality of a person is allowed to epitomize itself in a crucial incident. This event or incident might have no antecedents or consequences, and yet it should set forth in some unforgettable and inimitable way the soul of a man. It is our impressions of actual people coming to us in this way that give us the strongest and most irrefutable convictions that man is immortal. They have their roots in fiction through which we see our friends. Specific cardinal numbers are said to have similar indifference to other numbers and an independence that results from this indifference. They are the souls of things, both immanent and efficient causes of their being. It is on some such basis that we come to have lucky or unlucky numbers, perfect numbers, and sacred numbers. Dostoevski's Idiot and the sacred number seven are examples of such cardinality. In some sense they are internally substantiated and radiant of their own essences.

The senses in which this is true are not hard to ascertain, and their explication may on that account be disappointing. There are two main modern doctrines, revivals of ancient Greek theories, to account for this magic. I shall give them separately and briefly and then offer a combination that seems to me adequate to the theme here developed.

The first one is based on the notion of a class which has other classes for its members, in short, a class of classes. This conception has beautiful subtleties which recommend it to a certain type of mathematical philosopher who wishes to see numbers applied. It is like one of those ingenious tools which has a handle and any number of attachments to be added or dropped as the operator wishes or as the use dictates. Application and practice subtilize ideas. As morals led medieval theology into what for us is irrecoverable subtlety, so industry and applied science lead our mathematics into fantasy. I shall make use of the machinery here only to facilitate the approach to the mathematical object.

A cardinal number is the class of all those classes that have a given form. Suppose A is a class which has subclasses a, b, c, . . . as its members. Each of these classes may have members. A is a cardinal number if the subclasses a, b, c, . . . have the same form, and that form is a monad, dyad, triad, or a tetrad. That a class has one of these forms means that its members will be respectively singles, couples, or trios. For instance, the cardinal number one is the class of all those classes whose members are singles; the number two is the class of all those classes whose members are couples; and so forth.

This definition has been criticized for its circularity: it uses numbers to define numbers, since the monad means one, the dyad two, and so forth. There are two answers to this criticism. First the circularity is admitted but justified on the ground that the notions are ultimate and well enough understood in themselves to warrant circular or merely verbal definition. The other answer goes on to define the forms in terms of the relational structures of the ordinal series. The ordinal series can be broken into segments, and the relation within a given segment will define the form of a corresponding cardinal number. For instance, the relations in the segment from ordinal o to ordinal 2 yield the dyad, the relations in the segment from o to 3 yield the triad. Such parts of the ordinal series provide the forms for the subclasses of the corresponding cardinal numbers. Therefore, for every ordinal number there will be a cardinal number whose form is derived from a segment of the ordinal series beginning with o and ending in the given ordinal number. In terms of operations, the cardinal number represents an operation constituted of all the operations that developed the ordinal series up to a given term. The cardinal number five is the set of relations which generate the ordinal segment $(1, 2, 3, 4, 5)$, or is the result of the combined operation $\{[(1 + 1) + 1] + 1\} + 1$.

But I suggested above that this complicated business of classes of classes was due to the engineer's love of applied mathematics. For him it is a very efficient device for subsuming things under numerical forms, since the lowest members of the subclasses are assumed to be things counted. I shall describe other devices for applying numbers in the next chapter. If we sweep away this scaffolding of classes, we can see that the essential cardinal form is nothing but a special selection from the chain of relations that constitute the ordinal series and their combination in a form. In ordinary practice such selection is always restricted to a set of relations anchored at one end in the term zero and extending to some later term in the series. This is an arbitrary restriction. The cardinal form may bind together any terms in the series, and a cardinal number is any set of ordinal numbers properly related and taken together as a whole.

So far ordinal numbers have been taken as fundamental. If cardinal numbers are taken as fundamental, the ordinal numbers can be derived from them by analysis. An ordinal number can then be defined by its relations to other ordinal numbers within the structure of a given cardinal number. Either approach to the theory of numbers is good, but the latter seems to do the mathematical object greater justice.

So it is with the ordinal and cardinal elements in a story. The storyteller operates on a set of elements, the incidents, which arrange themselves usually in some temporal order. Then characters begin to take shape. Still the author who sees himself as a craftsman only claims he has presented only a story. If he is more sophisticated and critical, he will recognize his characters and watch them remake the story. Finally, they will take the work completely out of his hands and create their own situations. His characters have then become cardinal and their action dictates the ordinal structure of the story.

The same thing happens in less narrative forms of literature. A sonnet starts out to be a pattern of words, but it ends in a couplet that confers its significance on the whole poem. An essay starts as an exposition of facts and turns into a structure of ideas interpreting a problem. In Mr. Bertrand Russell's philosophical writings there is a persistent attempt to keep to the ordinal level; this is a large part of the secret of his clarity. But at some point interpretation, usually some bad metaphysics, threatens to come in, and we catch him protesting too vehemently that he is not a system-builder. Mr. George Santayana, on the other hand, almost never condescends to the ordinal level of detailed exposition. He moves among cardinal ideas and loads his words with complex, even moral, interpretation.

As it happens, recent discussions of form in the novel approximate this theory of numbers. It seems that there are two ways of analyzing a story corresponding to the two methods I have noted of introducing characters. In one the story is a series of events that happen to a character or group of characters. Such series may be very complicated and each situation may have many elements, but the characters are to be understood as having flat mirrorlike reflecting surfaces accurately recording the incidents and their relations. Action for such a character consists in the particular quality his reflection confers on the incident. We see through his eyes and it is in his vision that the material of the story takes form. The character itself is only a reflecting background. Such characters have been called "flat"; they are at their best in the satirical or comic novel.

In the other analysis of the novel the character is cumulative. It is as if each incident or episode had changed the quality of the reflection by giving the mirror an increasingly complex texture. Actually the events seem to come from the character. The internal structure of the character at any stage of its development consists of a set of habits, virtues, sensitivities, and powers that not only record but continually transfigure the preceding course of events. All of these are brought to bear on the immediate situation, and action consists in an internal drama merely conditioned by external affairs. The relations within are like the relations in the whole story, but transformed by projection on a smaller and more complex background. Such characters have been called "round"; their function is tragic.

But flat and round characters in comic and tragic plots do not throw much light on the contemporary problems in the criticism of fiction. They give an interesting classification to classic novels of the past, but even there the classes are not mutually exclusive, and many novels can fall outside of both. One can very well describe the spirit of contemporary fiction by saying that the novelist has the choice of producing the comic effect by tragic devices or producing the tragic effect by comic devices. The fact is that the novel is at present attempting to be that ideal combination of tragedy and comedy about which Socrates spoke that morning after the Symposium at the house of Agathon, the Athenian playwright. "Aristodemus was half awake and he did not hear the beginning of the discourse; but the substance of it was that Socrates was driving them to the admission that the same man could have the knowledge required for writing comedy and tragedy, that the fully skilled tragedian could be a comedian as well."

I should like to suggest that the solution might come from an insight into the nature of the ordinal and the cardinal elements and their respective functions in the novel. The suggestion is that the ordinal character should serve as the thread or ordering principle for the materials of the story, while the cardinal character is the weaver of the plot catching the parts of the events as they pass, transforming and organizing them into an internal dramatic pattern which mirrors the whole. At present it is the fashion to take the order of events from some social science, and then attempt to superpose a personality pattern taken from the psychological laboratory or clinic. The novel is a curious combination of sociological essay and clinical report. Tom Jones has become a sentimental idiot and Prince Mishkin an epileptic buffoon. The advice of the mathematician would be to take some arbitrary but interesting order of events, and then build the cardinal characters out of the elements selected and recombined as dictated by the author's genius for distortion and projection of human beings. Lewis Carroll's Alice is a model. Perhaps such advice would be more tactfully offered to a critic, suggesting to him what might be looked for in the more successful novels of, say, a Dostoevski or a Marcel

Proust. Cardinality of characters is an excellence proper to fiction.

Perhaps a reference to geometry will integrate the two perspectives of the mathematical object so far attained. Geometry tends to emphasize the constancy in the mathematical object. Each new variation reestablishes this constancy by disclosing a new feature in it. Arithmetic starts with these special features and weaves a network of relations between them. The transformations and developments in projective fields proceed by definite steps in a sequence fixed by rules based on these relations. Constancy is thus reincarnated in the relations and in the order and structure they confer upon the variations. The special devices of each mathematical discipline are fitted to pass from one emphasis to another in clearly marked successive steps of the analysis. Poetry often grasps the patterns of these steps, and consequently the structures so discovered, and presents them, as in the case of cardinal characters, integrated in crystalline insights.

The fact that mathematical formulae and poetic insights are believed to contain hidden meanings is a natural result. That one can tell long coherent stories is at first an amazing discovery. That these flights of imagination and logic lead to unsuspected existences does not long go unnoticed. It leads immediately to the breathtaking generalization that the secret of nature, the universe, all possible experience, is in these stories, and that numbers, figures, ideas, or words are always effluxes from things. This in turn means that the as yet unknown is making itself known in hieroglyphs. The universe is not only a system of perspectives, but also a book of mathematical formulae or a realm of poetic insights.

Perhaps one of the most amusing of these faiths is numerology. Correlating the letters of the alphabet and the digits from 1 to 9, repeating the numbers until the alphabet is exhausted, one has a table of translation. Any name can be transliterated to numbers. Then, adding the numbers and manipulating them according to rules, one can extract the "essential number" from the name. This number expresses the essence of the person who possesses it. Then by another table describing the characteristics of the numbers, the person will also be described. Thus it is learned that you, John Brown, are a number 2, and that 2 is practical, energetic, healthy. This tells you that you ought to be in business which is more suited to your character than your present occupation, say, teaching English literature in a high school. If you are having difficulties with your superiors or are a bad disciplinarian, this will sound inspired or scientific, as the case may be. You change your occupation and tell your friends how happy you are. They buy a book on numerology, and the cult arises whose gospel is a distant and weak caricature of Pythagoreanism.

More serious examples are found in modern developments of humanistic science. Economics and psychology are the best known repositories of this sort of wisdom. A society is translated into index numbers, or a personality into the terms of psychoanalysis. The retranslation is made into terms of applied morals and one becomes a Republican or Socialist, a married man or a divorcé, to the glory of mathematics and poetry.

Modern physical science is another case, whose forebears are astrology and alchemy. The story of how they came to be will need some more careful analysis. The next chapter is concerned with that.

I HAVE TRIED to present two aspects of the mathematical object, the constancy of figures throughout regular transformations, and the rules of order governing the variations under such constants. These two aspects are often taken to be the subject matter of mathematics and are called, respectively, space and number. Recently it has become fashionable to recognize their common nature and call it the continuum. The rest of mathematics is then treated as if it were a set of puzzles, presented in this subject matter, and solved by a corresponding set of tricks. This is a professional view of the matter and is justified by the demands of technical education. It trains people to solve problems and get results.

There is another point of view—most eloquently put in Plato's *Republic*. Beginning with the principles for the deployment of troops and the building of bridges and fortifications, or the weighing and selling of goods and keeping accounts, the student of mathematics ascends from the sensory world to the questions of what figures and numbers are, by way of a hierarchy of mathematical disciplines, each of which is a little nearer than the former to the pure things of mathematics. Each level is related to the next higher as the world of sense objects is to the whole field of abstract mathematics. Anyone who has studied mathematics to understand rather than to use, will know what Plato is driving at, but not all will follow the theological trend that early Christians saw in it and developed. I do not think Plato himself would have viewed such a development with complaisance. Mathematics has more in it than such ascetic edification. It is more like poetry, I again suggest. Added words in good poetry effect more adequate revelations of the poetical object. So in mathematics, added theory and calculation effect new manifestations of the mathematical object. This may, by chance, involve greater abstraction and bring about a more comprehensive integration, but it need not, and often does not. The method of the next two chapters is prompted by an attitude between the extreme Platonist and the professional mathematician.

The symbolic key to many mathematical treasures is the ratio. Like many of the elements in Plato's lower mathematical disciplines, ratios are useful and hence familiar in mechanics, but they also have liberal functions, leading to elegant and abstract discourse in its own right.

At this point there is a fortunate linguistic bridge between poetry and mathematics. It was built in antiquity by the Greeks and Romans and apparently was overlooked and forgotten for many centuries. Just when its disuse became general, I do not know. I would like to know because I believe it a very important, perhaps unfortunate, crisis in human thought. I believe it tells us something about modern thought.

What we call reason was often referred to by the Greeks as λόγος and by the Romans as *ratio*. We refresh our classical memory by associating "logical" and "rational" in English. Lying back of these words are distinct but related *Weltanschauungen*. The search for the meaning of *logos* among the Greeks led to a scientific and speculative habit of mind ending in scientific observation and speculative thought. The following of reason among the Romans led to the ethical and religious theory under which we still live. *Logos* is still commemorated in the names of most of our sciences; *ratio* goes with our popular and practical argumentation. We rationalize.

The Greek *logos* also means "word" and in general "discourse." The Latin *ratio* means "cause" as well as "reason." These are the linguistic hinterlands. They meet on the frontier on a bridge built by mathematics. The Greeks contributed ἀνὰ λόγον signifying a technical conception thus defined by Euclid: "Magnitudes are said to be ἀνὰ λόγον to one another which are capable, when multiplied, of exceeding one another." The Romans called the same thing *ratio* and took over the word *analogia* to cover the corresponding figure of speech. It will in some sense be a restoration of the bridge if we name it "analogy" and show its mathematical and poetic constitution.

Analogical thought is so common that we are surprised, like M. Jourdain, to learn that at any given time we are speaking analogy. It has many disguised appearances, some guarded by habit and convention, and some very obvious and open to exposure. I shall have to limit the catalogue to some well-known figures of speech, namely the metaphor, the simile, and the allegory. There are many other forms starting with the Homeric epithet and the Aeschylean adjective and ending with impressionistic and contemporary nonsense verse. If I did not have too many literal-minded friends, I should say that any proposition or significant sentence contained an analogy in some form or other. To escape the wrath of these, and also the more aesthetic of the poets, I will confine myself to a type of analogy midway between its two extreme forms. This type is at present called scientific language. To show it in its more extreme form, I shall take examples from the so-called humanistic sciences.

Here are seven metaphors:

> Man is a system of electrons.
> Man is a machine.
> Man is an animal.
> Man is a bundle of habits.
> Man is a soul.
> Man is an angel.
> Man is divine.

You can measure your progress in the school of modernism or hard-headedness by putting the word "dead" opposite any of these that you think are literal, and the word "alive" opposite those you think figurative or only partially true. You score one hundred per cent if you mark only the first "dead," and you approach o as you include more in this category. If you, as I, think they are all metaphors, you are just philosophical and a little mad.

It is a commonplace in logic that the copula "is" is a weasel word, and therefore it must be rendered unambiguous before the proposition in which it occurs is dealt with. I shall not go into the doctrine of categories here except to make an application of it. In all these metaphorical sentences "is like" ought to be substituted for "is." Each metaphor will then become a simile, and my meaning will be clear if I say that metaphors are suppressed or elliptical similes.

This leads to further scrutiny. The other words in the sentences need expansion. A "system of electrons" is a very short formula for the account a biophysicist would give of a human body. His account can be briefly formulated as "a collection of unit charges of electricity holding those relations to each other that are described in physical chemistry." "Man" will then mean a "physical body of certain size and shape," and the whole metaphor ought to read thus: "The parts of the physical body ordinarily known as man are to the whole body as the unit charges of electricity are to the electrical field which contains them." The metaphor, previously shown to be a suppressed simile, is now a suppressed analogy. The search for greater explicitness in the formula would lead to more elaborate expansions which would stop only when the present stage of physical science has been exhausted.

Likewise, the other metaphors could be analyzed and expanded by referring the right-hand side to one of the fields of knowledge which has had due attention from human beings at some time in the past. "Man is a machine" would refer to the science of mechanics. "Man is an animal" to biology. "Man is a bundle of habits" to one or more of the current psychologies. "Man is a soul" to ancient and medieval psychology and theology. "Man is an angel" to angelology, and "Man is divine" to one of the theologies or sociologies. Your judgment of the literalness or the figurativeness would depend upon which of the sciences has dictated a metaphysics to you. If you are not careful, you will find yourself mixing metaphors and believing something like the Irish Member of Parliament who said very persuasively, "I smell a rat, I feel it in the air, and I will nip it in the bud." Such is the result of ignoring metaphysical difficulties for the sake of facts and practical affairs.

This is analogy. Before it runs away with our thoughts, it may be well to give it a definition. It is the statement of the identity or similarity of at least two relations. It says, in symbols, that the relation of A to B is the same as the relation of C to D. Of course these relations may be of any degree of complexity, provided the identity or similarity is not violated. The complexity may be increased or diminished, apparently without limit. I shall call this property of analogies their expansiveness.

Such expansion seems to have no limit, but on the other hand, analogies get stretched. They sometimes break. But since they are very elastic, they usually do not break until they have become extremely tenuous and elaborate networks, so that the fragments are often very finely wrought products of human art.

The most obvious of these expansions is the allegory. The analogy has been expanded and stretched until finally the left-hand side has been torn away and the other remains, fantastic, enigmatical, fascinating, by itself. Stories from the ancient epics and their nourishing legends and sagas down to the modern novel and its nourishing morals and sciences are allegorical. It is the worry of the individual and the task of the critic to find the other halves of these figments of analogical lore. The orphan fragments may lose their hereditary distinguishing marks, and as a consequence mixed allegories are as common for most of us as mixed metaphors for Irishmen or Greeks.

In European thought Greek tragedy set a fashion, and Christian theology from the early church fathers to the contemporary modernist has kept it going in spite of many lapses into literal-minded interpretation of the texts and commentaries. The portrayal of an heroic figure who takes on himself the sins of his ancestors and carries out the consequences to a divine dénouement can be taken from the Greek stage and seen in the legends and myths of a whole people. An historic figure may be the hero and the events in his life transfigured by analogical expansion into a cosmic drama in which each character is a tragic hero and every event a purgation. The late middle ages saw an extraordinary inflation of this analogy. St. Thomas, starting with the names of God, had extended analogical knowledge to include nature, and his followers and opponents conspired to make the extension thoroughgoing and exact. Even outside the stream of strictly Christian thought every realm of discourse became phosphorescent, impregnated with floating idea. Everything meant not only itself, but something else ad infinitum and to the glory of

God. In the course of this exploration, the old bridge between imagination and mathematics was sure to be rediscovered. So it was. The Cabalistic and the Rosicrucian studies, together with alchemy and astrology, were midway of the bridge, and in one grand rush the whole realm of figure and number was taken over. This addition acted like a precipitant on an unstable chemical solution. Out of it came our modern science. The rest has steadily fallen into forgetfulness, disrepute, or opaque ritual. An analogy was stretched and broken, and we now have a mathematical-physical allegory on our hands and in our heads, and we are hunting for the rest of it, the lost symbol.

It is a little mysterious how all this happened. Man had been connected with the universe not by one but by an infinite set of ascending allegories, which had been understood and loved with subtlety and a discriminating skepticism. Suddenly, in a century, the whole structure collapsed; the clouds of glory condensed to numbers and measurements. We may be able to see how and why this happened if we analyze what is left.

"Magnitudes are said to have a ratio to one another," says Euclid, "which are capable when multiplied of exceeding one another." This definition has a subtlety at which modern mathematicians have wondered. In the first place "magnitude" may denote both numbers and figures or parts of figures. As we shall see it is itself a condensed mathematical analogy, and may refer not only to numbers and parts of figures, but also, when expanded, to apparently nonquantitative things. It anticipates analytic geometry and science as well. It thus may not exclude the lost poetry from which it came.

But a finer subtlety lies in the phrase, "capable, when multiplied, of exceeding one another." The uncriticized use of analogies had resulted in intellectual tangles before, and this phrase had been the means of disentangling ancient mathematicians from a mathematical scandal. This phrase allows for the rational treatment of the so-called irrational numbers. It brings these numbers under the control of rigorous symbols. It might have said "capable of equaling one another" and then the irrationals would have been excluded, and consequently great generality sacrificed in the conception. The definition will be clearer if the latter expression is included with the former. It will then read "capable when multiplied of equaling or exceeding one another." As it now stands, it is elegantly simple. It means that two numbers, lengths, areas, volumes, et cetera are in ratio when there is some multiplier or factor which applied to one of the magnitudes makes the resulting product equal to or greater than the other. The great power in this notion is due to a property of the operations of multiplication and division that I noted in the chapter on numbers. From the point of view of the theory of operations, multiplication and division are simple integrations or summations of complex combinations of elementary operations such as that represented by $+1$. From the point of view of postulate theory, multiplication and division are accurate and delicately discriminating selections of complex relations between elements. The ratio abstracts and fixes these relations and manipulates them without actually carrying out the operations which they make possible. It abstracts the bare relations. The irrationals are amenable to manipulation by ratios simply because of this abstraction which does not demand a completed operation. $1 : \sqrt{2}$ thus has a meaning as a ratio, that is, the relation between 1 and $\sqrt{2}$ is definite even though $\sqrt{2}$ is indeterminate as a rational number.

This abstractive property of ratios is further brought out in the proportion which, very simply defined, is the statement of identity or similarity between two relations each of which holds between two or more magnitudes. Here no relation of identity or similarity is stated between the elementary magnitudes, that is, the terms of the proportions, but the relations between these terms are said to be identical or similar. Thus A, B, C, and D may range over the whole field of numbers, and yet it may remain true that

$$A : B :: C : D.$$

This is the strict mathematical form of the analogy, but even this strict form is capable of great versatility without losing its accuracy or elegance. For instance, once the relations in the proportion are grasped, it is immediately seen that one can take it by alternation: A : B :: C : D is not violated if we say A : C :: B : D. Inversion produces another variation B : A :: D : C and by combined alternation and inversion C : A :: D : B. Also A ± B : A or B :: C ± D : C or D. This is by composition and division. Further we may have a continued proportion of many ratios such as A : B : C : D :: E : F : G : H or A : B :: C : D :: E : F and these can run through the poses of alternation and division and their combinations. Add to this the possibility of substituting numbers, lengths, or any suitable magnitude, for the terms in the proportions, and the loss of allegories seems quite compensated in its mathematical offspring. In fact, close scrutiny of science shows unmistakable family resemblances between it and its theological and literary forebears.

But the greatest historical exploitations of analogy are in the field of mechanics. Archimedes and his study of the lever, following the literary exploits of the Greeks, and Galileo's and Kepler's study of nature in its larger dimensions following the theological exploits of the middle ages, throw an interesting light on the region of poetry and mathematics that is often called exact measurement. Its importance in contemporary thought merits rather special attention.

Archimedes laid the foundation of a very permanent, at least a recurring, form of intellectual equilibrium by studying equilibrium in its physical forms. The problem is epitomized in the lever, and the principle of the lever is a proportion.

It is a well-known principle to the child who has teetered on a seesaw and to the merchant who has weighed small quantities of material goods in a balance that the heavier of the two weights must be nearer the fulcrum. That such a practical maxim is the shadow of a proportion was known by many of Archimedes' predecessors. It is such a commonplace with us that I hardly know how to convey the import of its theoretical basis. Perhaps it will be best to point out that it is the result of two apparently unjustified leaps of imagination. How far the leap was encouraged by the use of such things as scales and cranks I do not know. But a double leap it is, and the reader can supply whatever theory of revelation, reincarnation, or conventional fiction he prefers, to account for it.

To say that $W_1 : W_2 :: D_2 : D_1$ is by itself ambiguous. Perhaps it only means that certain numbers stand to each other this way:

$$2 : 4 :: 3 : 6.$$

In that case it is merely a happy discovery in arithmetic. But W stands for weight and D stands for distance. It may therefore mean that the relation between two weights is the same as the relation between two distances. But this is not true for many relations; for instance, "heavier than" is a relation between two weights, but not between two distances. The only relation that works is a hybrid combination of these two.

The combination is evidently derived from two previous proportions, namely:

$$W_1 : W_2 :: 2 : 4$$

and

$$D_2 : D_1 :: 3 : 6.$$

Then because we already know in arithmetic that $2 : 4 :: 3 : 6$ we can finally see how it is that $W_1 : W_2 :: D_2 : D_1$. But why weights and distances are like numbers, to use the simile, has still to be explained. The only answer that I know is that some poet of the commonplace was playing with words, and somebody took him literally. That "somebody" was an engineer and became famous for what he could do with wonder-working machines. Archimedes was a later follower who saw levers in everything, just as poets sometimes see people in the sky. The modern folk who see vitamins in food, and vibrations in personalities belong to minor schools of this sort of poetry.

The most spectacular and convincing school is, however, that of the more natural sciences which now names Galileo, Kepler, Newton, and others of the Renaissance as its originators. They saw other proportions in things and like Archimedes generalized boldly. Their style has greater subtlety and the accompanying mathematics finally gets very complicated.

Being accustomed to think of celestial beings without body or visible form, yet present at places and times, they had a somewhat wider field for speculation and experiment. Aristotle had said that the time of a body's fall is proportional to its weight—a fairly corporeal notion. Galileo saw a different factor involved, not a mere velocity such as Aristotle saw, but a more ephemeral property which he called acceleration. This is really a ratio between two velocities and he found that for any given interval this ratio is equal to the ratio between the squares of the distances covered. The formula $V_1 : V_2 :: D_1^2 : D_2^2$ was the visible sign to convince men of the real presence of forces causing the acceleration. That forces were *verae causae* thus became a dogma believed by every scientific man till fairly recently. Not only was this true of falling bodies, but of all moving bodies. There was the force of inertia keeping bodies at constant velocities, and other more active forces, among them gravitation, changing their velocities and directions as they were able, in proportion to themselves. Galileo said he read these secrets in the book of Nature. Mathematics was only the code in which they were written. It is difficult to know whether he was a poet or a mathematician. He was like a modern engineer watching and making things act in certain ways and at the same time seeing schemes and meanings in things. The fact that he saw these in the scales and dials of his instruments hardly substantiates his reputation for skeptical experimentalism. There is a conflict here between mathematics and poetry that should after all these years be familiar. In fact it is so familiar that we ignore its metaphysical sins and call it the scientific spirit.

Another man before the time of Galileo had the same combination of traits, with the conflict even better concealed. Tycho Brahe had been looking at the stars across the sights of his instruments and writing down the numbers that appeared on the scales. He said the numbers represented the positions of the stars. Such procedure is a curious medley of ratios between lines and angles of observation, points on charts and places in the sky. He had written one of those finely wrought medieval allegories of the sky in the numbers of arithmetic. But it had been done in the finest "scientific spirit."

Johann Kepler had worked with and after him on this allegory, having in mind the less scientific, but more mathematically elegant model of the solar system fashioned by Copernicus. Kepler added the lore of conic sections that had come down from the Greeks and a touch of sun-worship from Zarathustra. With their aid he translated and condensed Tycho's allegory into three mathematical analogies:

(1) The orbit of a planet is to the sun as the circumference of an ellipse is to one of its foci.

(2) The areas swept by the radius vector (the line from the planet to the sun) are proportional to the times of revolution.

(3) The cubes of the mean distances of the planets from the sun are proportional to the times of their revolution.

It is perhaps surprising that Kepler substituted angels for the forces which Galileo had seen in the motions of more terrestrial bodies, but the reasoning from the evidence is the same. The only difference is that Galileo took an engineer's liberty with the tradition for which Kepler had a poet's love and piety. In other words Kepler was a less self-conscious poet.

It is often said that Newton saw the force of gravity in an apple. Byron assigns the origin of this insight to the piety of Newton and his preoccupation with the Biblical account of the fall of man. I shall not be so Byronic. Newton's poetic and mathematical heritage came from his more immediate past. His preoccupation with ratios is more relevant, although it may be admitted that Biblical literature and numbers have often been fine intellectual companions and emotional auxiliaries to each other. It is certainly true that he connected falling apples, cannonballs, and space in general with celestial bodies, both astronomical and divine.

Nevertheless, it was his extraordinary ability to disentangle the chain of abstract relations from the more exotic and wayward speculations of his predecessors in the school of natural analogy that led to his summary and perfection of their work. He made the analogical jump that astrophysicists are now making daily, from Galileo's art of physical experiment to Kepler's astronomical inferences. He did it by careful consideration of their ratios and a judicious sorting of their literary allusions. He finally kept all their mathematics, Galileo's forces, and Kepler's conic sections. Consequently the law of gravitation is an extraordinarily condensed version of the allegory of nature. We are still searching for the lost symbol that goes with Newtonian mechanics.

It is not the aim of this book to show that mathematics is identical with poetry, but it will do the reader no harm to read mathematics as if it were poetry. The following are some propositions from Newton's

Principia. Mechanics is here set forth as a poem to be read, I maintain, as a litany.

From the *Mathematical Principles of Natural Philosophy*

BOOK I

DEFINITIONS

DEFINITION I. The quantity of matter is the measure of the same arising from its density and bulk conjunctly.

DEFINITION II. The quantity of motion is the measure of the same, arising from the velocity and quantity of matter conjunctly.

DEFINITION III. The *vis insita*, or innate force of matter, is the power of resisting, by which every body, as much as in it lies, endeavors to persevere in its present state, whether it be of rest, or of moving uniformly forward in a right line.

DEFINITION IV. An impressed force is an action exerted upon a body, in order to change its state, either of rest, or of moving uniformly forward in a right line.

DEFINITION V. A centripetal force is that by which bodies are drawn or impelled, or any way tend, towards a point as to a center.

DEFINITION VI. The absolute quantity of a centripetal force is the measure of the same proportional to the efficacy of the cause that propagates it from the center, through the spaces round about.

DEFINITION VII. The accelerative quantity of a centripetal force is the measure of the same, proportional to the velocity which it generates in a given time.

DEFINITION VIII. The motive quantity of a centripetal force, is the measure of the same, proportional to the motion which it generates in a given time.

AXIOMS, OR LAWS OF MOTION

LAW I. Every body perseveres in its state of rest, or of uniform motion in a right line, unless it is compelled to change that state by forces impressed thereon.

LAW II. The alteration of motion is ever proportional to the motive force impressed; and is made in the direction of the right line in which that force is impressed.

LAW III. To every action there is always opposed an equal reaction: or the mutual actions of two bodies upon each other are always equal, and directed to contrary parts.

. . . .

Book III

Propositions

Proposition I. That the forces by which the circumjovial planets are continually drawn off from rectilinear motions, and retained in their proper orbits, tend to Jupiter's center; and are reciprocally as the squares of the distances of the places of these planets from that center.

Proposition II. That the forces by which the primary planets are continually drawn off from rectilinear motions, and retained in their proper orbits, tend to the sun; and are reciprocally as the squares of the distances of the places of those planets from the sun's center.

Proposition III. That the force by which the moon is retained in its orbit tends to the earth; and is reciprocally as the square of the distance of its place from the earth's center.

Proposition IV. That the moon gravitates towards the earth, and by the force of gravity is continually drawn off from rectilinear motion and retained in its orbit.

Proposition V. That the circumjovial planets gravitate towards Jupiter; the circumsaturnal towards Saturn; the circumsolar towards the sun; and by the forces of their gravity are drawn off from rectilinear motions, and retained in curvilinear orbits.

Proposition VI. That all bodies gravitate towards every planet; and that the weights of bodies towards any same planet, at equal distances from the center of the planet, are proportional to the quantities of matter which they severally contain.

Proposition VII. That there is a power of gravity tending to all bodies, proportional to the several quantities of matter which they contain.

Proposition VIII. In two spheres mutually gravitating each towards the other, if the matter in places on all sides round about and equidistant from the centers is similar, the weight of either sphere towards the other will be reciprocally as the square of the distance between their centers.

Proposition IX. That the force of gravity, considered downward from the surface of the planets, decreases nearly in the proportion of the distances from their centers.

Proposition X. That the motions of the planets in the heavens may subsist an exceedingly long time.

HYPOTHESIS I. That the center of the system of the world is immovable.

PROPOSITION XI. That the common center of gravity of the earth, the sun, and all the planets, is immovable.

PROPOSITION XII. That the sun is agitated by a perpetual motion, but never recedes far from the common center of gravity of all the planets.

PROPOSITION XIII. The planets move in ellipses which have their common focus in the center of the sun; and, by radii drawn to that center, they describe areas proportional to the times of description.

PROPOSITION XIV. The aphelions and nodes of the planets are fixed.

Certain more prosaic things are to be noted in this sketch from the history of mechanics. First, motion is the quarry for which a net is being fashioned. Certain philosophers beginning with Zeno have always said that no net could catch the quarry. The answer has been persistently given that, as a matter of fact and practice, mechanics does catch it. According to the present account the secret of the answer lies in the ratio and proportion which constitute the soul of mechanics. They bring some of the speculative boldness of poetry into measurement. Depending on the sweep and fineness of mesh in the net of proportions, enough of the whimsicality and infinite detail of nature is caught to make an impressive display. If we do not catch motion itself, we catch its path, and if we do not follow the path step by step, we follow it in leaps and bounds; if at the end it is no longer motion that we have, but rather its ghost, that is good mathematics and good poetry. What really happens is a puzzling translation of concrete event, fact or experience into a set of abstract relations which are symbolized and expressed in the sciences that claim to describe our universe. The symbols which effect this translation are ratios in proportions. The only evidence there could be, that the translations are accurate and the results true, would have to be formulated in still other proportions. By ratio and proportion our knowledge of the universe stands or falls.

This point can be more emphatically stated as follows. Quantity or magnitude as a property of things is a condensed result of analogical reasoning. When we ask, how much? the answer we expect and are satisfied with is a mathematical metaphor. Five pounds means that some physical object is to some other physical object (the standard weight) as five is to one. When we ask for the certification of the standard, we go with John Quincy Adams and his associates to the stars and the proportions that describe them.

But the importance of quantity and measurement in mathematics is habitually overestimated by the scientist and the engineer. Ratios and proportions are by no means all of mathematics. Just as poetry would be poor indeed if it spoke only in analogies, so mathematics would be even more clumsy and platitudinous than poets think it is if it calculated only in proportions. The conclusion is that if mathematics is more than proportions, quantity is not all of the mathematical object, but rather only one part.

I imagine that the reader's patience has been tried by the general tone and manner of this chapter. If so, he is sharing the writer's feeling about the subject matter. There is something very puzzling and disconcerting in it all. I suspect it is very near to what is often called the magic of poetry and at the same time the riddle of the universe. I even suspect that the two are one, and that Kant's famous remark that two things he viewed "with ever increasing awe, the starry heavens above and the moral law within," is also concerned with the same thing. It is the old Platonic problem of the relation between things and ideas. We seem to build castles in the air and recognize their fantastic unearthly character. We then turn to nature to find a local habitation and a name for them and ourselves. But we find nature and experience allegorical. Whatever direction we search to find literal truth, it always leads to the same eerie destination.

I should like to postpone facing this problem indefinitely, since it lies beyond the "scope of this book"; but to do so would be to lose the force of the argument in this chapter, and in a sense to miss the point of the whole book. I shall therefore try to answer the question that inevitably arises at this point: What is a literal statement? The only answer that is possible within the limits of the present subject matter must come by stripping rational discourse of its apparently figurative accretions and saving what is left—if indeed it is anything at all.

To begin with it seems that many important things can be defined in terms of analogies. For instance, from what has been said thus far we may derive the following definitions:

(1) Measurement is an analogy that asserts the similarity of two relations, one between things and the other between numbers. Example: Distance A is to distance B as 1 is to 10.

(2) Quantity is the condensation of an analogy of measurement into a numerical metaphor. Example: Distance B is 10. The inverse of this expresses an occult property: 10 is distance B, or 10 is perfection.

(3) A machine is a body the motions of whose parts are reciprocally proportional, or a machine is a body the relations between whose parts are similar to the relations between numbers in a proportion. Example: The lever.

(4) A scientific instrument is a machine whose parts vary from their states of rest or uniform motion in proportion to forces impressed from outside. Example: The chemist's balance.

(5) A scientific law is an analogy, or system of analogies (allegory), which asserts that the relations between things is similar to the relations between numbers. Example: A lever is in equilibrium when $W_1 : W_2 :: D_2 : D_1$.

(6) Science is an allegory that asserts that the relations between

the parts of reality are similar to the relations between terms of discourse.

(7) The natural universe is the things and their relations that enter into the allegories of science.

In these seven definitions it can be seen that poetry and mathematics are constituent parts of those analogies and systems of analogies that we call scientific knowledge. Scientific objects are poetic objects whose relations are said to be similar to the relations between mathematical objects. This means that reality, in so far as it enters rational science, corresponds to the terms and relations in an analogy.

This leads to the serious proposal of a logistic that would provide a basis for scientific method. The first postulate of such a logistic system would state that any proposition in the old logic would be a metaphor subject to expansion into similes, analogies, and allegories. Such expansion would provide terms for the expression of any universe of discourse as an allegory whose atomic elements would be ratios. If there is objection to generalizing the term, ratio, in this fashion, we might speak of *logoi* as the constituents of allegories. It should be noted that such logical atoms are merely unit elements, not absolute simples which cannot be analyzed. They are atomic only relatively, that is, with respect to any given allegory.

The advantages of this terminology would be many. Let me note a few of them. First, it has long been noted that analogies play a large part in scientific thought, but, due to the loose terminology used in many arguments by analogy, it has been supposed that analogies themselves are untrustworthy. The fact that mathematics has achieved such remarkable advances in rigor and accuracy by means of ratios and proportions, as will appear in the following chapters, should quiet such fears. The admission of poetic analogies to intellectual respectability would confer similar intellectual responsibilities on the darker side of scientific thought. There seems to be no reason to suppose that they would not be fulfilled.

Second, the problems involved in measurement, use of instruments, observation, and verification in scientific method could be more clearly seen in terms of analogies. The definitions I have given of some of the constituents of scientific technique are capable of refinement, but even in them some usually unnoticed presuppositions of science are manifest in a rather startling way.

Third, the recent attempt to popularize scientific knowledge and the scientific attitude of mind has paralleled a revival of interest in the critical methodology of science. It now seems that the popular educational movement has had a rather unpleasant recoil in the mind of the technical scientist. The difficulties in translating mathematics into expository literature have uncovered terminological confusions in the laboratory itself. These difficulties have been seen first in the loose analogies of the popular version, but it is admitted that analogies are also used as scaffolding for the construction of the hypotheses to be tested by experiment and are apt to come out with the conclusions that result from the experiment. The passing of the classical analogy of the engineer's model is compensated for by elaborate imaginative pictures, or the purely operational interpretation expounded in Bridgman's *Logic of Modern Physics*. All of these are more or less poetic analogues for mathematical notions. The problem of "physical interpretation" of mathematical formulae is an integral part of scientific method, and could be clarified and ordered by a properly formulated calculus of analogies. Such a calculus might lead to a more fruitful and systematic exploitation of the historical notions in science which now return to the laboratory almost by accident and by the back door.

The obscurantism of occult and pure mathematics has been continually purified by formalization. A similar purification of scientific thought is badly needed at present.

This leads back to the question that I promised to face: What is a literal statement? Curiously enough, literalness is to be found in the more elaborate expansions of figurative statements. The literal interpretation of a proposition is to be found in the allegory. Early in this chapter it became clear that the peculiar function of the ratio was to isolate and abstract relations from their geometric and numerical contexts. The expansion of metaphors to allegories fulfills the same function in a poetic subject matter. Expanding analogies progressively reveal relations; argument by analogy is the fundamental technique in the process of abstraction. This should be clear from a former illustration. The proposition, "man is a machine," if it is taken as a statement of fact, is obscure and ambiguous. It is an allegory condensed and badly crushed. Properly expanded it is the explicit detailed analysis of a man's body, an allegory stating that the temporal and spatial parts of the human body are related and articulated according to the laws of motion. On one side of the allegory we have a diagram of the body and on the other side we have the abstract formulae that describe its motions. The farther the expansion is carried out the higher the degree of abstractness and explicitness achieved. If the allegory could be completely expanded and one side separated from the other, either side would be a literal statement. But curiously enough, the expansion can take place only when the two sides are allowed to interact symbolically; a *logos* or *ratio* in one must suggest and lead to the discernment of its analogue in the other. There seems to be no end to this process and therefore no end to the expansion. A purely formal and therefore literal statement is never possible. Pure poetry and pure mathematics, like pure music, are never expressed. The extreme case would be symbols expressing themselves, but even there the distinction would have to be made between symbols as things and symbols as ideas. Discourse is allegorical or nonsensical.

For the poet facts, like words, are symbols, and knowledge consists in the insight into the symbolic relation. For him the world is a poem to be read. Its laws are the laws that govern his words. For the mathematician and the scientist facts are to be referred to principles and causes. The allegorical correspondence of his ideas with the facts is the truth. The world is a network of relations which his formulae reflect.

Perhaps the question about literal statements should not have been answered here. At any rate now that it is answered after a fashion, it will be well for us to go on to further complications of mathematical and poetic analogies. We shall find that the proportion and the analogy are fundamental in what follows, and that even what has gone before is picked up and reorganized in an allegorical medium. An algebraic equation is a complex pattern of ratios, and the corresponding poetic forms are expanded metaphors. Mathematical and poetic objects wear that sort of clothes.

5 ❧ EQUATIONS

THE STATEMENT that ratios are fundamental in mathematics was not intended to be a promise of what is to come in the following chapters. It would certainly not be agreeable to the professional mathematician who knows how cumbersome and awkward the more advanced parts of mathematics would be if they were treated with the calculus of ratios. Still it is surprising and important to realize that very many of the fundamental conceptions in the "higher" mathematics were first defined as special combinations of ratios. In many cases the original meaning is lost, but this is merely another way of saying that the new terms and conceptions have absorbed and reinterpreted the old.

For example, the science of trigonometry, or the measurement of things by triangulation, is founded on three simple ratios. In any right triangle each of the acute angles can be measured by the *sine* which is defined as the ratio of the opposite side to the hypotenuse; or it can be measured by the *cosine* which is defined by the ratio of the adjacent side to the hypotenuse; or finally, it is measured by the *tangent* which is defined by the ratio of the opposite side to the adjacent side. Each of these measurements of an angle by lines involves a proportion, and the constituent ratios can be extracted and rear-

ranged in new formulae. If the hypotenuse is arbitrarily given the
value one, then, by the Pythagorean theorem, the square of the sine
plus the square of the cosine is equal to the square of the hypotenuse
which is one. This is the fundamental law in trigonometry; by suitable manipulations it can be expanded into the other laws by means
of which any part of the intelligible universe can be reduced to numbers. Plato's prophecy in the *Timaeus* that the world could be made
intelligible by transcription to a system of right triangles is fulfilled
in this science.

But this use of ratios goes considerably beyond the rules for proportions that one would find in any textbook of arithmetic or geometry. In the first place, the laws of trigonometry are formulae that
combine ratios as numbers are combined in arithmetic. This means
that ratios have been substituted for numbers and come under the
control of the arithmetic operations, addition, subtraction, multiplication and division. Trigonometric calculation has absorbed more
notions from arithmetic than proportions could use. The resulting
formulae themselves are much more like allegories than they are like
simple analogies.

Further, the ratios are treated as if they were fractions according to
the special rules for reduction to lowest terms and similar transformations. Both ratios and fractions gain in significance and power by
this combination, and with it another mathematical notion, variation,
has crept in unnoticed from geometry. Figures vary in geometry and
because of their variation can undergo transformation. Numbers were
brought in to formulate the order of their transformations, but variation itself was left unformulated. It is involved in these trigonometric
formulae and as a matter of fact is fundamental in any complete account of proportions. The proportion really states the principle of
such variation. It says that one ratio is substitutible for another. Thus,
$1 : 3 :: 4 : 12$ means in terms of fractions that $\frac{1}{3} = \frac{4}{12}$ and we

might go on indefinitely equating equivalent fractions. In some sense geometrical figures in the same field of projection or group are alternative expressions for one thing which is equally manifest in each, just as these fractions are representative of some generalized quantity. This one thing that the proportion indirectly symbolizes is called a variable and may have a special symbol, such as x, y, etc. Special classes of numerical expressions are said to represent its possible values. A variable is said to have an unlimited number of values which together constitute its field of variability. The values may be other variables, but are usually understood to be numbers, or expressions containing numbers. Numerical values are called constants in contrast to the variables whose field they constitute.

Thus, when ratios become terms in arithmetical or algebraic formulae, they exhibit new properties in addition to those recognized explicitly by Euclid. They still retain the properties they had in proportions, but they are also variables subject to the more general rules of algebra and arithmetic. This increased generality is the first property to be noted in the terms of mathematical allegories. It is nicely exemplified in the theoretic power of trigonometry.

Descartes begins his *Geometry* with considerations like these. From the time of the Greeks the more complicated parts of mathematics had been handled by ratios and proportions only. Euclid had written two separate books of the *Elements* on proportions, one dealing with numerical ratios, and the other with geometric ratios. He had seen the possibility of applying one to the other, but had kept them apart to insure more thorough treatment. He had expanded the metaphors of measurement, but had kept their constituents distinct. On the other hand Archimedes and Galileo had learned much both in arithmetic and geometry by combining them with a third analogue, nature. They had proceeded back and forth between numbers, figures, and natural objects, discovering and tracing down relations in a triple allegory. Descartes resolved to restrict himself to arithmetic and geometry to discover the secret of the allegory.

He began with an old problem of Apollonius: To find the position of a given point relative to a given set of straight lines. It was for Descartes a problem in proportions. Instead of measuring each distance and tabulating the result, he extended the lines until they intersected and made triangles. He could then state the distances from the lines to the point in ratios and proportions. The result was a collection of interrelated proportions which he simplified by the rules of arithmetic into a single formula consisting "of terms, some known and some unknown, some of which were equal to the rest; or rather all of which taken together are equal to nothing; for this is often the best form to consider." He called such formulae equations.

In this manipulation he had performed a peculiar, though mathematically familiar, trick. He had expressed the relations between distances without knowing or trying to discover their specific numerical values. It will be recalled that ratios allow this since they indicate arithmetical operations without requiring that they be actually completed. In this case the trick has peculiar consequences. The formula actually gave him the solution of his problem, namely the relative position of the given point with respect to the set of lines, but it also gave him the position of an "infinity of points" which satisfied the same conditions. The formula was too general; it selected a whole class of points instead of only one. He suspected that the unknown terms had something to do with the superfluous generality. This suspicion led to a discovery that had greater importance than the original problem. Formulae could be made to select and describe specific classes, or infinities, of points that constitute well-known geometric figures. As it happened, he had before him an old friend, a conic section. He tried the trick on several other sets of lines, and found that he could derive the equations not only for the other conic sections, but also for more complicated curves. There were evidently equations for every geometric figure.

Further analysis uncovered just what was involved in this discovery. It had long been known that a line could be defined as the path of a moving point; that a plane is the path of a moving line; and that a volume is the path of a moving plane. Lines, planes and volumes, so defined, are called loci. The infinity of points might then be understood as the positions occupied successively by a point moving under specified conditions. Geometrical instruments, such as compasses, parallel rulers, and other devices that had previously interested Descartes embodied such conditions for the construction of figures. Descartes happily recalled that these instruments also embodied ratios and proportions like those he had combined to solve the problem of Apollonius. Following this clue he assumed that the equations expressed the conditions governing the generation of loci; loci and equations were the two analogues constituting the geometrico-algebraic allegory.

For instance, he found that a parabola is a locus of a point such that its distance from a fixed point, called the focus, is always equal to its distance from a fixed line, called the directrix; the corresponding equation is $y^2 = apx$. The ellipse is the locus of a point such that the sum of its distances from two fixed points is constant; its equation, $\frac{x^2}{a^2} + \frac{y^2}{b^2} = 1$. The circle is an ellipse whose two fixed points, its foci, are identical: $x^2 + y^2 = r^2$. The hyperbola is the locus of a point such that the differences of its distances from two fixed points is constant: $\frac{x^2}{a^2} - \frac{y^2}{b^2} = 1$. These definitions, like the equations, summarize very complicated analogical reasoning. Almost every term is a metaphorical expression for a proportion. We shall see that the theory of conic sections in analytic geometry expands these statements and integrates them in an allegory of still higher degree of complexity.

It remained for the analyst to show the specific correspondences between the separate elementary terms in each side of the allegory. There were knowns, or constants, and unknowns, or variables, in the equations. This distinction had been found important in measurements. But measurements involved a scale. So Descartes set up an artificial scale for the measurement of his curves. He chose two fixed lines perpendicular to one another, and marked off unit distances on each. By means of triangulation he measured a locus. In this way the constants became known in terms of the unit distances on the scales, and they turned out to be the numerical conditions governing the generation of the locus. Further, the roots of the equation, that is, the values for the variables, measured the distances of the points on the locus from the axes. The infinity of values corresponded to the infinity of points. The variables under the control of the constants allegorically represented the locus.

One further point in the allegory must be noted. Descartes said that the best way to understand the equation was to think all the terms together as equal to nothing. This does not mean that the equation disappears, but rather that in this way the form of the equation was more adequately seen. Descartes was interested in the forms of these equations; such an interest should accompany the allegorical method. In this case the allegory that Descartes discovered shows that the equation and the locus have the same form, a principle of great importance but not easily observable. Stating the equation in some standard fashion, with all the terms together and with the distinction made between variables and constants, facilitates the necessary abstraction. Then it can be seen that the principle governing the variation of the variables is the same as the principle that governs the generation of the locus. Finally, the form of the equation itself emerges and can be compared or contrasted with the forms of other equations, term for term. In fact, the form turns out to be itself a variable whose values are special equations that are equivalent to each other in certain respects, just as equivalent ratios are values for a variable. The class of similar equations taken together constitute a manifold allegory. This leads into the second and perhaps more important part of analytic geometry where equations are distinguished and classified systematically. Before we go on to that, it may be well to record some points in literary criticism, the algebra of poetry.

The origins of mathematical and literary forms always make interesting and controversial theory. Mathematics is on the one hand said to have been revealed to priests and on the other to have been derived from surveying and commerce. Descartes worked in natural science, and the project for an analytic geometry was proposed to him by an angel in a vision. Likewise the drama was a religious ritual demanded by the gods, and yet it pictured the social and economic conditions of its devotees. In both cases the activity of an allegorical mind is discernible, whatever the conclusions about origin are, and the allegories come into the genetic theories as the original logical insights which are arranged by the historical mind in a temporal order, so that the first allegory contains the original form from which the others grow. If we reverse the argument, the conclusion is that at least form is present and can be isolated and analyzed.

As far back in the history of drama as we wish to go, dramatic form is found reflected in things and reflecting them in turn, and its constituents are abstract terms more or less easily recognizable even in the presentation on the stage. Aristotle says that characters in Greek tragedy are a little better than ordinary men, and the characters in comedy are a little worse. They are types, I suppose this means. On the stage the actors wore masks containing megaphones to insure a formal aspect and a dignified manner. Comedies use corresponding devices to sharpen the formal presentation.

Further, the persons of the drama are usually limited in number, and are embedded in a set of conventionally determined relations. Each character has a definite capacity for a certain set of motives and acts which fill in the pattern of the play. A role is defined within its range of possible events by constant relations between characters and between characters and circumstances. A dramatic character is a variable in a dramatic equation acting with other characters under constant conditions to determine the plot of the play. This applies to both modern and classic drama as well as to the marionette stage or the Punch-and-Judy show. A game of chess with its pieces and their possible moves and the sequence of their plays is a limiting case which illustrates the breadth of the principle. The items in the "dramatis personae" and the "argument" or "preface" are the usual ways of acquainting the audience with the formal demands that the play-wright, the producer and the actors satisfy as their abilities permit. The dramatic critic discusses many other things, but the degree to which form has been grasped and realized decides. As algebra is to arithmetic and geometry, so is the drama to narrative forms of literature. Algebra marks the discovery of variables and forms; the drama isolates and emphasizes character and plot.

The notion lying back of "the persons of the drama" contributes to the theory of the novel that we discussed in Chapter IV. It introduces the notion of a variable character or dramatic type, that aspect of a character that remains identical and establishes continuity throughout the narrative development. The ordinal and cardinal aspects of character emerge from the story like figures in the projective field of geometry. They register and epitomize the passage of events, but at the same time they are manifestations of more general characters that run through the development, just as points fall within a locus and numbers are substituted for variables in equations.

The ordinal character is passive to events; the cardinal character achieves a certain independence and power of initiating action; but it is the variable character that achieves the independence of generality and informs the whole story. It is the interplay of variable characters that constitutes the plot, or form of the drama. Furthermore a variable character can step out of one story and into another, or out into the familiar world of human experience, where it recreates itself whenever human material and circumstance give it content. Thus we understand our friends and ourselves *sub specie aeternitatis* in terms of dramatic types and the world is populated with Oedipuses, Don Quixotes, Fausts, Falstaffs, Hamlets, and Bovaries. They are dramatic ideas which, once embodied, never die.

Any character may on analysis show three aspects: the ordinal which merely reflects the passage of events; the cardinal which works them over and transforms them into action; and finally the variable which informs the action with ideas. They are rather like the vegetative, animal, and rational souls discovered by Aristotle.

One is tempted to speculate on the possible consequences if Descartes had carried out his project of applying his analytic method to human morals. He could have found his material in the theater and the literature of the stage, and gone on to develop an analytic geometry of the soul. He himself might have become a great dramatic critic or a Jungian psychoanalyst defining the orders and types of human character. Perhaps it is just as well that he went on with metaphysics.

One of the more important results of the discovery of form and the isolation of variables in equations has been a greater freedom in mathematical styles. The ratio and the proportion achieved a certain freedom by substituting numbers for numbers, ratios for ratios, and geometric magnitudes for geometric magnitudes. The success of ancient mathematics and early science was due in part to that freedom. But the equation provided new machinery for the interchange of terms. The emphasis on the unknown terms as variables tempted the adventurer with symbols. If a variable can be manipulated as a blank term, restricted only by the rules for algebraic operations, all sorts of tentative substitutions can be made and the consequences watched. Descartes and his successors found that a given equation could pass from one form to another by suitable substitutions. Substitutions may be divided into two classes: those which do not violate the form of the equation; and those which do change its form. The former might be called regular and the latter irregular.

Transformations of both sorts have occurred in literature. For instance, the history of European literature shows a continual interchange of values in the pattern of Greek tragedy and comedy. I have already pointed out in the last chapter how the form of tragedy is expanded and binds medieval theology together. Similar transfigurations have come to special characters in the plays of Aeschylus, Sophocles, and Euripides. They are not only immortal; they have had many reincarnations. In Aeschylus' *Furies*, Orestes is caught in the dilemma of vengeance and comes increasingly under the influence of otherworldly creatures to his mental discomfiture, his practical undoing, and final judgment. The elements in the situation are simple, the complication obvious, and the dénouement necessary. It is the formula of the Greek tragedy which is so powerful in its extreme simplicity. By the time of Dante the motif has reached its greatest allegorical expansion and it blossoms into the infinitely complex expression of the *Divine Comedy*. Each variable in the original formula is still present, the original sin, the fall of man, the struggle for redemption amid the horror of hell and purgatory, the thwarted love of woman and deity, and the graduated blessedness of a just heaven. Dante expanded the formula by substituting mankind for Orestes and the whole cosmos for the ancient Greek world. The change in physical dimensions suggests the change in poetic depth.

The actual distance from this to *Don Quixote* is in terms of atmospheres very slight, as it is in time, but the change is crucial. Lucian in his *True History* had tried a similar change, but it was trivial in comparison with Cervantes' achievement. Their method was to make irregular substitutions. Lucian's *True History* and Cervantes' *Don Quixote* revel in the irrelevance of irregular substitution. In place of the moral problem and the need of redemption we have the crushed paper flower of knighthood, and ennui. In place of Electra and Beatrice we have the far-off loves of medieval romance embodied in a lady of doubtful reputation and in serving maids. In place of the hierarchy of furies, demons, and angels we have the mistaken identities of the countryside. In place of the way of sorrow and repentance we have the series of mad adventures encountered by the valiant knight, Don Quixote de la Mancha. In spite of the tone of burlesque there is the high seriousness demanded by Aristotle in great tragedy.

I shall not burden the reader with the details of the later transformations of the Orestes formula. As Descartes says very often in his *Geometry,* the reader will understand better and enjoy more if he makes his own discoveries and applications. I suggest Shakespeare's *Hamlet,* Flaubert's *Madame Bovary,* and Dostoevski's *The Idiot* as relevant exercises. Sinclair Lewis's *Main Street* and almost any play of Ibsen are easy to begin with.

It is in the more extreme types of irregular substitution that we find the secret of poetic humor. In recent years there have been many serious books written on this subject. They have been concerned chiefly with a psychological explanation of laughter. The logic of humor has been neglected. It would run somewhat as follows. Some formal pattern is invented, such as Greek tragedy, and a great deal of imagination and thought is poured into the mold. It becomes classic. Then a substitution is made which explosively breaks through the form. The Greek satyr play and comedy illustrate the result. New wine is poured into old bottles and there is laughter when the bottles break. Cervantes, Boccaccio, and Rabelais produce more subtle transformations. Their substitutions mix the tragic and comic forms and result in the marvelously fertile forms of the modern novel.

Descartes made another use of irregular substitution. His substitutions broke through the old forms and established new forms of higher generality and greater inclusiveness. In his hands irregular substitutions became the means of discovering the higher genera for the species of equations already discovered. It is now evident that Descartes' chief work was the second part of his analysis; it has led to a complete classification of equations. The method is called the "discussion of equations."

He first made the distinction between the variables and constants in the formulae resulting from his combinations of ratios. He then noted that the variables occured in multiplicative relations with themselves. In his *Geometry* he wrote such terms as products thus: $x \cdot x \cdot x$. We now write such terms with exponential numbers, thus x^3, and call the exponential number the power of the variable. It designates the number of times that the given variable is to be taken as a factor in the product. When no number is given it is to be understood that the power of the variable is one. Equations can then be divided into *orders* according to the highest exponential numbers occurring in them. An equation containing a third-powered variable is of the third order. It is interesting to know that the order of the equation corresponds to the number of lines used in the original geometric derivation of the equation.

Having ordered equations according to the powers of their variables,

Descartes went on to subdivide the orders into *types* which correspond to the manner in which the constants contribute to the form of the equation. For this purpose he distinguished between two kinds of constants. Some of these resembled variables in that they could be generalized for purposes of discussion and consequently might take on more than one value, but they also resembled constants in that they were assumed to be single-valued for any formal manipulation of the equation. These he called arbitrary constants. The other constants were numbers; these he called absolute constants. Constants of both kinds entered equations as factors in products with variables or as separate terms. In using constants to distinguish types it is sometimes necessary to assume that a term is missing because it has zero as a factor; it is then formally present though notationally absent. Constants occurring as factors are in general called coefficients.

By means of these distinctions and the appropriate symbolic conventions it was possible to state what are now called general equations which represent the form that an indefinite number of similar equations may embody. For instance

$$A x^2 + B xy + C y^2 + D x + E y + F = 0$$

is the general equation for all conic sections. It is an equation of the second order according to the highest exponential number it contains. A, B, C, D, E, and F are here arbitrary constants; for purposes of discussion they represent substitutible numerical values. If numbers or absolute constants are substituted for them, the various specific equations for the conic sections will result. Thus if zero is substituted for A, B, E, and F and some numerical values other than zero are substituted for the remaining coefficients, we have the equation for a parabola. For instance let $C = 1$ and $D = -8$ and we have the parabola, $y^2 = 8x$. Other substitutions produce other conics.

These arbitrary constants and the numbers which may be substituted for them are vestigial remains of the ratios which determine the locus of the equation. Descartes knew this and succeeded in formulating general rules in terms of them for abstracting from any equation the differentiae of the types of equation of any given order. For the conic sections these rules are as follows:

If in an equation of the second degree

$B^2 - 4\,AC = 0$, then the equation is a parabola;
$B^2 - 4\,AC < 0$, then the equation is an ellipse;
$B^2 - 4\,AC > 0$, then the equation is a hyperbola.

$B^2 - 4\,AC$ is therefore called the "characteristic" for conic sections. The method which applies such rules to general equations is adequate for the classification of any equation that may occur. It is the basis for a great deal of the work that has been done on equations. Some such scheme is a necessary adjunct to any use of analogy or allegory to prevent errors and misuse of formulae. It is also true, but often ignored, that some insight into form is necessary for the solution of even the simplest problem in applied algebra, mathematical or poetic.

It seems that a rigorous "discussion" of the forms of literature might aid in literary criticism, where there is so much confusion about standards of classification. Now some sociological, historical, psychological, or naturalistic criterion is applied before it is analyzed and understood. No doubt these criteria contain rigorous formulae in terms of which discrimination is possible, but who knows what a literary "characteristic" is?

Aristotle defined in fairly rigorous terms, which have often been misused, the forms of Greek tragedy. There have been attempts to go on where he left off. These attempts have approximated a parallel with the analytic methods of Descartes. The dramatist has used analogies to abstract his forms from his materials, and the critic has isolated and formulated general formulae in terms of types of character and constant conditions, the conventions and limitations of writing and production. All this might be pushed further if the method itself were better understood.

For instance, within the general form of Greek tragedy, Aeschylus' Orestes might be defined as a variable character whose acts are equally determined by practical and imaginary or theoretic considerations. Antigone is a variable character whose acts are determined more by imaginary or theoretic than by practical considerations. Clytemnestra is a variable character whose acts are determined more by practical than by imaginary or theoretic considerations. Then one might go on to the content of such formulae in terms of cardinal and ordinal elements in each type of character. Whether the results of such analysis would be useful or not I do not know. The analysis itself, I do know, has the same fascination that mathematics has. Perhaps some committee of censors would lobby a bill through a state legislature requiring that all publications have their formulae printed on their jackets—a pure literature law. Publishers' salesmen could psychoanalyze their clients and prescribe the proper literary purchases. A worried critic might even be able to decide whether a novel or a play is art or not.

Descartes did not know what utility was hidden in analytic geometry, but this is what he said he had done; he is giving the geometric statement of the allegory:

"But it is not my purpose to write a large book. I am trying rather to include much in a few words, as will perhaps be inferred from what I have done, if it is considered that, while reducing to a single construction all the problems of one class, I have at the same time given a method of transforming them into an infinity of others, and thus of solving each in an infinite number of ways: that furthermore, having constructed all plane problems by the cutting of a circle by a straight line, and all solid problems by the cutting of a circle by a parabola; and finally all that are but one degree more complex by cutting a circle by a curve but one degree higher than the parabola, it is only necessary to follow the general method to construct all problems, more and more complex, ad infinitum; for in the case of a mathematical progression, whenever the first two or three terms are given, it is easy to find the rest.

"I hope that posterity will judge me kindly not only as to things which I have explained, but also as to those which I have intentionally omitted so as to leave to others the pleasures of discovery."

There is prophecy in this last paragraph, but the events are more wonderful than the prophecy. As usual the analogical applications of the pure mathematical theory have been myriad. As it happens, the orbits of planets and comets, not to mention the paths of other less spectacular material bodies, are conic sections. Descartes himself went on to construct his own physics and astronomy, in which the properties of matter are essentially exemplifications of equations. Physicists still pay tribute to Descartes by referring all their discoveries in the laboratory to his realm of equations. There is now said to be a general equation for the motion of any particle of matter anywhere in the universe.

But there is also in this quotation an atmosphere that would be called foreshadowing in the drama. There was a prophecy that analytic geometry itself would go far, and the suggestion that it would provide the map for still greater explorations in the territory of pure mathematics. So it has done. The classification of equations might be compared to Linnaeus' classification of plants and the map it provided for the biological explorations of Darwin and Wallace. Descartes' work was to be accepted and reinterpreted in terms of the calculuses of Newton and Leibniz and the modern developments in the theory of functions. The species of equations were still to find their places in an hereditary series. The next chapter discusses mathematical heredity.

6 ❧ FUNCTIONS

THE READER with strictly literary interests will have wondered for some time how long the writer of these pages would go on talking of the poetry in literature in nonliterary terms; in other words, where discussion of style is to find a place in this logomachy. For, after all, words are the elementary units of the poet's craft, and the light from mathematical theory is weak if it cannot lift the mystery from this dark corner in literary criticism.

It may surprise the reader to learn that it is just here that the problem of poetry and mathematics started up in the writer's mind, and that it has taken the roundabout road I have been traveling to come to anything like a solution. I approached the subject from logic and mathematics. In the attempt to find out what they were talking about I found the literary analogy most illuminating. Impressed and a little puzzled by that discovery, I was tempted to push the analysis of literature to the end. The result has been only to arrive at the beginning, but even there the reward is the discovery of what is at least for me a new dimension in literature, amenable to logical treatment and yet rich in what are known as literary or critical overtones. These overtones are usually discounted by the logician and credited to the deceitful ambiguities of words. It is thus that logicians and mathematicians are wont in their youth to escape from the siren of literature. Later in life they usually fall before her enticements and call the results of their delayed romance scientific philosophy. Words have in truth been their undoing. Some verbal Satan has come in the guise of the second person of the Trinity, Logos, and another intellectual sin has been committed by a garrulous old man. The current doctrine of emergent evolution is a case of this.

I have decided to deal with the verbal enchantress now. I am reassured by the appearance at this point of an important distinction and corresponding relation between poetry and mathematics. What is most abstract in poetry is most concrete in mathematics, and what is most abstract in mathematics is most concrete in poetry. Specifically, ideal character, its structure and its development, is abstract in poetry and corresponds to figure and number which are as near as mathematics ever comes to concrete elements and data. I am about to show that words and style which are concrete in poetry correspond to functions, the typical abstractions of mathematics. Further, it appears that what is most essential in each, the poetic and mathematical object, is most adequately expressed in words and functions respectively. I believe the end of our wandering is in sight in this thesis.

If I were to adduce evidence for it, I would have to draw it from several studies that "fall outside the scope of this book." I refer to that family of genetic studies that goes by the name of philology, in which the interplay of geography, physiology, psychology, sociology, and anthropology weaves scientific myths and legends around our words and what they mean. A study of the part played by scientific instruments in the choice of mathematical symbolism is most needed in this field at present. But I am always dissatisfied with the inconclusive conclusions of these studies. They are themselves mathematical and poetic stories and therefore beg my question. I shall therefore state the thesis as if there were no evidence for it and let the reader use his own good sense in judgment.

The problem of style, as it actually faces a writer, is the difficulty in finding words to fit a subject matter. There is a rightness and a wrongness about words that is inescapable, yet in the end ineffable. Essays on style often speak of word-values, emotional connotations, sense of language, tones of voice, experience with the classics, even verbal inspiration, and refer the inevitabilities of style to these creative factors. Which or how many of these are involved, I do not know, but I am convinced that the ever present and crucial factor is a subject matter which is the dictator of practice, and the standard of judgment. The problem of style is the fitful faithfulness of symbols to an ideal subject matter. The mathematician and the poet have had long experience with it, and their products are the facts to be considered.

On the side of theory, I propose to turn two traditional doctrines, one philosophical and one mathematical, to the end of educing the basic principles of a science of style. Such a science might be called, by analogy with music, linguistic harmony. It would contain the dialectical conclusion of this argument about poetry and mathematics. The doctrines that I propose are to be found in idealistic logic and infinitesimal calculus, respectively. I might derive both of them from the philosophy of Leibniz, but for purposes of exposition other sources are more useful.

The incidental suggestion for using idealistic logic comes from a criticism that is usually accepted as its refutation. It is said that idealism is a philosophy founded on grammar, and that its metaphysics contains the fallacy of imputing grammatical conventions and rhetorical forms to reality in general. Suppose we accept the point as regards logic and let the metaphysics go. Idealistic logic should then show us at least the structure and ideal function of language, and in the end we should discover what are the significant connections between words and their meanings.

The criticism with which we start was first directed by the idealists themselves against what they took to be Aristotelian logic. Aristotle in one of his definitions of substance had said that a substance is that which cannot be predicated of anything else, but of which other things are predicated. By this he is supposed to have identified substance with the grammatical subject of a sentence, and to have vitiated the rest of his logical theory. Supposing he did do that, what follows?

John Locke, a reformer of medical theory and practice, a critic of Christianity, a social theorist, and a generalizer of what he took to be Newtonian scientific method, showed to his own satisfaction that any substance of the sort that carried attributes or qualities could not be known, but only inferred, and that anything known immediately in experience would be a quality only. He then proceeded to divide qualities into different kinds. There were primary qualities, those talked about in physical science and therefore independent of our experience though capable of appearing there; and there were secondary qualities which always depended on our sense organs as well as physical objects for even their existence. Locke further divided primary qualities into classes which he called solidity, size, shape, and motion; and secondary qualities into classes whose names were taken from the various senses which gave them their existence. These distinctions were not original with Locke, rather with Galileo, but they became the foundation of idealistic logic in his writings.

After Locke, Bishop Berkeley and David Hume successively broke down these neat conventional divisions and left the qualities in a near-chaos whose only remnant of order came from the rather weak laws of association. Our experience contains objects only because we are in the habit of associating ideas by their similarities, differences and their succession in time and space. Substance which had been an unknown x in Locke's critique is now only the ghost of primitive mental habits of such association.

All this, if it is the logic of grammar, means that all words are adjectives whose behavior and company are determined only by accidental associations. If style is at all relevant, it means that it is a matter of chance. At best style can be no better than experience in its order and excellences. What is skepticism in the theory of knowledge is nihilism as regards literature.

But skepticism and nihilism clear ground for new building. As in the textbook history of philosophy, Kant comes next. That he also follows Leibniz may not be wholly irrelevant in a discussion of the logic of grammar. Kant showed how Hume's skepticism was somewhat sentimental and melodramatic, that, with a little closer analysis, the laws of association were enough to give us back our real objects, or at least permanent substrata to which qualities and attributes could belong in our minds. In the course of the demonstration he also listed the meanings of the word "is," to which I referred in the chapter on analogy, and believed he had found a limited number of possible ways for combining substances with qualities, and qualities with qualities. These were his categories, and together they revise Aristotle's grammar so that it becomes the canon of style for Newtonian physics.

But Kant's substance was a bit ghostly and his categories were too neat. Later logicians found more meanings for "is" until finally Hegel realized that there were an infinite number of them; also that Kant's substance was itself adjectival. He organized a method for dealing with these infinite qualities and categories. They would now come in threes, a positive, a negative, and a synthesis of the two. He used the resulting style to write a history of the human spirit, a fine demonstration of what a style can do to transform a subject matter.

However, Hegel's architecture was too heavy for the quick changes that literature and logic have to make. F. H. Bradley saw the problem. He accepted the merely adjectival function of all words and discourse, but proceeded with more caution and subtlety than his predecessors to invent some general but still versatile method for discovering the delicate organization of words into propositions, propositions into systems, and systems into universes of discourse. He worked with three criteria in mind, coherence, inclusiveness, and concreteness. It should be remarked that his own style admirably fulfills these criteria, but for him they were properties of thought, to which discourse must be faithful. Adjectives must not contradict each other, any adjectival unit must include as many sub-adjectives as possible, and the generality must not violate the distinctions in the detail of the subject matter. It might well be said that F. H. Bradley wrote logic like a literary critic and his brother, A. C. Bradley, wrote literary criticism like a logician. The implied comparison with William and Henry James is not unjust.

The result of these studies in the logic of adjectives may best be stated in terms of a recent theory by W. E. Johnson, who himself is not an idealist, but has availed himself and logicians in general of some of the insights of the idealists.

If we say something is red, we speak accurately only if the something is also colored. The applicability of the adjective "red" depends upon the applicability of the adjective "colored." "Colored" is more inclusive than "red," and is therefore said to be a determinable and "red" is its determinate. Further, if a thing is red, it must also have some determinate shade or tint of red. Such a shade or tint would then be a determinate of "red" and a subdeterminate of "colored." "Green" is also a determinate of "colored" and might be called a codeterminate of "red." The distinction between "determinable" and "determinate" is of course only relative. That is, "colored" may also be a determinate, say, of the determinable, "visible." Similarly, a given shade of "red" may be a determinable for still lower determinates. It is important to notice that there seem to be no upper or lower limits to the adjectival hierarchy.

On the other hand there are distinct limits in the horizontal dimension. For instance, "sweet" does not belong to "colored," and "invisible" is wholly excluded from the hierarchy under consideration. In other words, the line between contradictories and the line between opposites mark outer boundaries and inner divisions respectively in any given family of adjectives. Adjectives thus have harmonies and discords similar to those in music.

It may seem foolhardy to try to apply any such wooden machinery to the subleties of style, but such an objection would be based on a misconception of the nature and function of logic. Logic does not dictate rules even to argument. It follows both argument and lyric as fast as it can, and records, analyzes and criticizes. Logic would be disgraced in its own home if it could not handle literary criticism. This theory, cumbersome and pedantic as it may sound, takes care of the most radical innovations in style, as well as the more plodding discourse of science.

Certain modern writers of verse delight in the mixture of sense departments, as in "echoing light." The problem that this raises for the logician is to locate the determinable under which these adjectival words will live in harmony. This example is rather like Dante. It may refer to a neo-Platonic universe where all ideas are antiphonal, or, depending on its context, it may invoke elements from the world of modern physics. The Homeric epithet, though conventionally accepted as commonplace, transports one to a special sector of the ideal sphere where dawns are necessarily connected with rosy-fingered goddesses. The more surprising and unique the combination of words, the higher and more delicate the abstraction achieved with no consequent loss of what are called concrete values. Thus poetic license and poetic justice play complementary guiding roles in the exploration of the realm of intellectual imagination.

Contemporary science which might be supposed to be conservative in such matters has just recently been outdoing the poets in its usages. "Warped space" and "motion without matter" are dictated by logical necessities of a subject matter which has outgrown the analogies of straight-line rulers and marbles. It is logic, not drugs or dreams, that justifies men in strange fantastic ways.

The school of idealism in philosophy met a crisis in the rise of the romantic school in literature. Newton's fluxional calculus and Leibniz' infinitesimal calculus mark the crisis in a similar game of mathematical tradition and innovation. These mathematicians practiced a license that roused the conventional mathematician and philosopher to protests comparable with classicist attacks on romantic experiments. It was in fact a romantic movement in mathematics, and its application in science and industry laid the conditions for romantic literature and gave a hint even for its style and atmosphere. But again it was not essentially a revolt against convention, but rather a fresh attempt to render symbols faithful to an ideal subject matter. Almost as an accidental consequence, it has revolutionized the whole of mathematics, logic, and philosophy, to say nothing of the physical sciences.

Newton was chiefly concerned with the analogy between the paths of projectiles and the orbits of the moon and planets. In order to work it out, he required some general method for expressing the rates of change in their velocities and directions; in short, their accelerations at any given instant and point. Galileo had used ratios to express such accelerations over given intervals. Newton's task was to get a ratio which could be applied at any point in the motion. For this he hit upon the notion that intervals might approximate points if they were allowed to grow smaller and smaller. If the ratio of acceleration for an interval could be caught just as the interval disappeared into a point, it would express the acceleration for that point without further consideration of the interval. Starting with the ratio for a given interval, he would allow it to vary with the decreasing interval, and watch its behavior until the interval disappeared. The ratio at the beginning was called a prime ratio, and at the disappearance of the interval, an ultimate ratio. Since it expressed the ratio of acceleration for a moving point, and was itself a variable quantity, he called it a "fluxion."

As on former occasions in the history of mathematics, what was needed was new symbolic means for handling ratios, and the solution was reached by indulging in mathematical license. New symbols were to come by the misuse of old symbols. The mathematician's technique in such a crisis is to close the eyes of his mind and follow his nose for symbols wherever it may lead; he can explain later what happened. In technical language an expression containing some irregularity is used as an operator on a known formula, just as $+1$ and -1 were used without question as operators to develop numbers. When some important transformation is made by this means, as in the case of the negative numbers, it is hailed as an invention, and becomes an established part of mathematical technique. Later someone explains what the operation actually does to the mathematical object and the result is then called a discovery.

The trick this time was to allow the denominator of a fraction, the second term in the ratio, to disappear. According to the rules of algebra such a misused fraction retaliates by becoming paradoxical or indeterminate. But in this case, if the sin were ignored, a very valuable expression would remain.

Thus the ratio, $\triangle y/\triangle x$, is an operator applied to an algebraic expression. As $\triangle y$ and $\triangle x$ grow smaller and smaller, "as small as you please," there emerges from the operation the desired expression. The sin is overlooked and the result is accepted and called a fluxion or differential, dy/dx for short. This operation was very successful in extracting the precious ratios from all sorts of algebraic equations, and was the foundation for a new branch of mathematics. Its success sent many minds in search of its theoretical justification in terms of an underlying relational structure.

But both the verbal and the algebraic accounts are paradoxical. Intervals after all are not points, no matter how small they become, and dy/dx actually contains an indeterminate expression, o/o. The mathematical classicists made fun of this "ghost of a departed magnitude," this quantity that was zero and infinity at the same time and yet had the appearance of an honest finite quantity. The theologians like Bishop Berkeley saw a fine opportunity for a *tu quoque* against their scientific critics who boasted of consistency and precision. Newton called his invention a fluxion while Leibniz, with a more efficient notation, called his a differential. Neither gave a respectable mathematical account and a long controversy was started and continued for more than a hundred years. It was further complicated by a professional attempt to assign credit for the invention to one of two people, neither of whom had a clear idea of what he had done.

The settlement of the main controversy had to wait until Dedekind and Weierstrass in the nineteenth century generalized the problem to include the scandal of the irrational numbers and the incommensurable magnitudes, such for instance as the ratio between the radius and circumference of a circle, or the ratio between the diagonal and a side of a square.

These bothersome numbers and magnitudes were first discovered by the Pythagoreans. They also had started such a controversy that the members of the mathematical cult made a secret of them. One man who divulged the secret was drowned on a prearranged sea voyage, it is said. By the Pythagorean theorem the diagonal of a square with sides, say, one inch long, has a length expressible only as $\sqrt{2}$, the square root of the sum of the squares of two sides. But $\sqrt{2}$ is neither a whole number nor a fraction. It is apparently no number at all. The simple and almost sacred square contains a mystery not open to Pythagorean treatment by numbers.

Euclid had a method of handling these numbers in proportions. I have noted this in remarking on the subtlety of his definition of a ratio. "Two numbers are in ratio which when multiplied are capable of exceeding each other." Although they do not become rational numbers, they could be handled in ratios and proportions. Dedekind took advantage of this notion of ratio and generalized it so as to redefine numbers both rational and irrational. He did it by means of a conception which he called a "cut" (*Schnitt*). This conception is necessary to make the Euclidean definition explicit.

He defines a cut as follows: If an ordered class C is divided into two non-empty subclasses C_1, C_2, such that every element of C is an element either of C_1 or of C_2, and such that every element of C_1 precedes every element of C_2, then there exists an element x which affects this division. Such a division of C into C_1 and C_2 is a cut. This means that any irrational number, say $\sqrt{2}$, corresponds to a cut of the class of numbers into two subclasses, the first of which contains all those numbers whose squares are less than two, the second of which contains all those numbers whose squares are greater than 2. ($\sqrt{2}$ can belong to either one but not both of these subclasses.) Obviously a whole or fractional number corresponds to a similar cut, and it is essential that it should.

The irrational numbers had been excluded because they were unending decimals whose exact value could not be ascertained. But if the essential properties of numbers do not require countability, but mere position, and the irrationals have the other properties that are essential, there remains no reason for excluding them. A further question remains as to where they belong in the series that we know. Dedekind's answer is that they go between the fractions, after those less than themselves and before those greater than themselves. No other objection of serious nature has yet been raised.

But there are more consequences. If you feel your feet leaving the solid ground of countable numbers, you have understood the point of Dedekind's definition, but you must also realize that you are merely shifting the whole number system to more solid ground. You will see that the essential nature of numbers, from the point of view of the theory of functions, is to be found in such relations as "greater than," "less than," "before," and "after." By means of these relations you have discovered a class of numbers that come between the members of the compact series of fractional numbers, and render the number series as continuous, as free from jumps, as we understand space to be.

It is not too difficult to transfer the rule from numbers to fluxions and infinitesimals; that is what Dedekind and Weierstrass did. Instead of trying to find some unique member of the number series corresponding to the differential, they redefined the differential in terms of relations. As in the case of numbers, this shift in definition gave the whole realm of mathematics a jolt and a reorientation. It revealed new properties of the mathematical object, and these new properties were soon seen to be fundamental.

The differential, or the fluxion, is the result of an algebraic operation on equations. Its unconventional and apparently illegitimate character comes from the old story of the mathematician following symbols in search of a new style and his return with intellectual trophies. When $\triangle y/\triangle x$ becomes dy/dx, it means that algebraic rules have given way to analysis of a new aspect of the equation, not hitherto isolated. This is the pure relational structure within which variables are merely obedient elements. An equation in stating the equality of sets of symbols expresses the relations that hold between classes of values. The numbers and points of analytic geometry emphasize these values. Although Descartes' attention was called to the relational aspects, his work ended in techniques of substitution and manipulation of values. It was in terms of these techniques that he passed from one type of equation to another. The effect of applying the notion of the "cut" to the differential was to throw the emphasis on the purely relational aspect of equations.

It is as if the philologist had been interested only in the meanings and derivations of single words, and had given his account of grammar and usage in terms of such atomic elements as phrases, sentences, and paragraphs. He would then be an etymologist. Suppose the grammarian suggested that the relations between words were the more important properties for linguistics. The philologist might then see that even the meanings of single words come from the structures in which they occur in discourse. The words are merely the points of reference in the context, each dependent on its companions for its own character. This would be an exaggeration, like saying that characters in a novel are nothing but the intersection of forces and lines of action in the plot. We are familiar with the fallacy in political science that says the individual is nothing but a creation of the political state. But it is nevertheless an important aspect of numbers, novels, states, and equations. It marks an advance in the direction of subtlety and precision of thought.

This new aspect of the mathematical object is called functionality. As soon as it is seen in the differential, it is applied to any equation, and as soon as it is seen there, it is extended to cover all statements or exemplifications of mathematical conceptions. The reader of these pages should not be wholly unfamiliar with it, for my exposition of the various aspects of the mathematical object has consisted in selecting perspectives on it which would show the functional characters in each case. The new definition of the mathematical object that comes to light has application to all that has gone before. x, y, etc., are said to be in functional relation when there is a law or form by which the variation of one or more variables determines the variation of the others. We now can write the formula for any mathematical element in terms of a function of one or more variables thus: $F(x)$, $F(x, y)$, $F(x, y, z)$. Thus we say $F(x) = x^2$ and $F'(x) = 2x$ where $F(x)$ means the original function and $F'(x)$ means the differential or, as we now call it, the derivative function.

Before we pass on to further developments of this in the calculus, it may be well to point out the various properties of single functions. First, they exhibit a constant or invariant form or pattern of relations. Second, they contain variables between which the relations hold. Third, on account of the constancy and variability in the pattern, the change of value in any subsumed variable brings about a corresponding change in the value of the other variables. It is rather too bad that Newton's term *fluxion* has fallen into disuse. It is a more descriptive term for the properties of functions. "Flowing magnitudes" catches an essential property not conveyed by "function."

Among many consequences of this interpretation is the much-discussed notion of relativity. The value of any variable is relative to the value of any other variable by virtue of the constant relations holding between them. We have not only equational functions, but also complicated system functions, and finally transformation functions for systems. Relativity is the most spectacular functional property noted in such systems as modern mathematical physics.

The calculus goes on to further consequences. Since derivatives are themselves functions, new or second derivatives can be found for first derivatives. Theoretically, there is an infinite number of such derivatives for any given function. Each derivative selects and isolates properties from the original function and the limits of such analysis are only those of ingenuity. At present such analysis ends, in practice, with numbers, which are considered constant in an arbitrarily absolute sense. But the series of derivative functions is ideally infinite.

Of course this series suggests its reverse. Any given function may be considered a derivative function, and there will be at least one function from which it is derived. Thus if $F(x) = 5 x^2$, $F'(x) = 10 x$, and $F''(x) = 10$, $F'(x)$ and $F''(x)$ are first and second derivatives. The reverse of differentiation is called integration. Starting with $F(x) = 10$, $\int 10 = 10x$, $\int 10x = 5x^2$, and $\int 5x^2 = \frac{5}{3}x^3$, by introducing arbitrary constants we may develop an indefinite number of variants on each of the integral functions. Thus functions belong in families having a vertical order constituted by integral and differential relations, each level of which has a horizontal order consisting of variants generated by the substitutions of arbitrary constants. The project stated by Descartes at the end of the last chapter is thus fulfilled in more elegant fashion than he had imagined.

The English mathematician Taylor contrived a formula for expressing these connections. The formula now goes by his name, Taylor's Series:

$$f(x) = f(x_0) + f'(x_0)(x - x_0) + f''(x_0)\frac{(x - x_0)^2}{2!}$$
$$+ f'''(x_0)\frac{(x - x_0)^3}{3!} + \cdots\cdots$$

In this series functions are treated as variables and substitutions can be made by which any function can be expanded and its properties revealed and marshaled for observation, as chemical compounds and biological functions are studied in the laboratory—perhaps with greater precision. Newton's Binomial Series is a case of this.

Of course there are literally myriads of applications of the calculus and the functions which it studies. Newton's success with physics promised much and the calculus has borne out the expectation. Most of modern physics depends upon the use of derivative and integral functions in differential equations. Here functions themselves are taken on as variables and the solutions found by a combination of algebraic and differential operations. The analogical inferences that can thus be drawn are truly miraculous.

Successful application of the calculus in the natural sciences led to many ambitious projects in other fields. Economists and sociologists found happy illustrations of functional relations in the statistical records of their observations. They have spent much time and energy in matching such records with conic sections and other functional symbols, and in hunting for more data to correct discrepancies. But perhaps the happiest thought found root in logic. Logicians for a long time had found fault with the propositions and classes of Aristotle's logic. Boole, the Irish mathematician, conceived the possibility of working out the parallel between algebra and logic. In this project Taylor's Series came in for attention and a variation on it was found most powerful in rendering the import of propositions explicit. There immediately appeared the term "propositional function." $f(x)$ or $\phi(x)$ now would represent a proposition whose form could be considered without reference to its content or values. Now it is possible to abstract such forms for any discursive statement and propositional functions have become the subject matter of logic. Logic and much philosophy have been rendered responsible to a more refined type of rigor. The revolution that this signifies has incidentally made even more clear what the subject matter of mathematics itself is. Mathematics is the science of relations as such.

These extensions suggest another application more nearly relevant to the present purpose. At least the intellectual basis of style in literature can now be made explicit. Style is an unconscious witness to the presence of a system of abstract relations among adjectives. Perhaps it is better not to tell the poet this, but it might be whispered to a critic.

There is a theory in metaphysics that ideas are floating singly; they are wandering adjectives. This most certainly is not true if the styles of the derivative and the poem are admissible evidence. Adjectives, and by adjectives I mean words in general, come together, or they are not significant, and therefore not words. They are selections from vast systems, the clouds of glory from the intellectual heaven which is our artistic home.

I do not mean by such expressions to drag in any super-Platonic metaphysics. The walk of a friend, the line of a melody, the healthy vibration of a motor are known when they are seen or heard. To most things of this sort we respond by a feeling or action. If we are poets, we speak and in some sense are possessed by these things. To put it crudely, we dance to their rhythms. But we are not these things. We are acting out an analogy and it is only their forms that possess us, maybe in body only, but sometimes in soul as well. When it is the latter we have discerned a function, and if we speak, we speak literature. In this way words and symbols are only the carriers and for the most part they are not very willing servants, not found at the proper time, or manipulated in harmony with what they symbolize. Here lies the problem of style. Few of us are poets or mathematicians; we do not think or speak poetry and mathematics most of the time. But when we and they are engaged in such happy activity, we are catching relations and realizing values, and our symbols in word or act are faithful to their subject matter.

This is where psychology, sociology, prosody, mathematical logic, and a thousand other unclassified studies throw light. They are concerned with the controlling constants of mathematics and poetry. They attempt to show the "how" of expression. They should not be condemned for not telling what gets expressed, nor should they claim that they do tell that.

This opens the way and demands attention to the metaphysics of this essay. For the most part it will be postponed to the next chapters, but a preliminary distinction can be made.

What is the difference between mathematics and poetry? I have been at pains to describe their meeting points, but have in no way intended to assert their identity. Briefly, the difference is this. The mathematician sees and deals with relations; the poet sees and deals with qualities. Functions and adjectives respectively are the symbols through which they see and with which they operate. Mathematics is analytic, seeing wholes as systems of relations; poetry is synthetic, seeing wholes as simple qualities. The qualities that the poet sees are due to relations, says the mathematician. They need purgation. The relations that the mathematician sees are concrete and factual, says the poet. They need appreciation and love.

The difference is possible because of the way experience comes, qualities in relation, substances with attributes, wholes and parts. Both poet and mathematician select and abstract what they see and in that they are free minds. Sometimes they, and almost always we, get confused, taking relations for qualities and qualities for relations. The result is belief.

Belief is the natural attitude of a thwarted mind. It arises from fatigue and confusion. The psychologist may tell us about fatigue, but the critic must point out the confusion. For the most part confusion is of two sorts, one involving symbols, and the other metaphysical nostalgia, the tendency of thought toward the absolute. The next two chapters view these regions from a distance.

7 ❧ SYMBOLS

IN THE FIRST CHAPTER the field of these critical excursions was roughly defined as the various attempts to deal with ideas by means of symbols. It was then postulated and it has been taken for granted throughout that the relation between symbols and ideas is such that poetry and mathematics are possible. It is now time to show what such a possibility involves.

The answer to the question requires a brief discussion of the aesthetics of poetry and mathematics. It is a truism that poetry has aesthetic properties, and it is true, though less often noted, that mathematics for a mathematician also has aesthetic properties. I have been at pains to show their intellectual properties, but I hope it has not obscured their more obvious and immediate aspects.

As a matter of fact aesthetic properties have appeared in the course of expounding the intellectual properties. In the discussion of geometric figures as projective fields, cones of light rays were cut by planes and the results were pictures. If the base of the cone was a disc, then the various pictures were specific circles, ellipses, parabolas, hyperbolas or pairs of straight lines. Working under geometric rules, analysis immediately follows the fixing of such static pictures and the pictures are dissolved into sets of relations; the emphasis is on intellectual properties. From the point of view of the artist or seeker for aesthetic objects these static pictures are destinations rather than points in progressive analysis. They are designs and forms to be reproduced in chosen media.

A recent critic of painting has shown how all the designs in pictures can be derived from the projective field developed from the spiral. By proper transformations within this field seven basic designs, each with infinite variations, are produced. More specialized bases such as the logarithmic spiral give rise to the designs of Greek vases and temples as well as many objects of nature. These aesthetic objects can be extracted from apparently strict mathematical considerations. They can be analyzed into mathematical relations and generalized, but their strictly aesthetic character as they stand is exhibited in their uniqueness and concreteness.

Literature is occupied with such objects and is concerned to present them as vividly and efficiently as possible. The literary realization, as in *Alice in Wonderland,* of any segment of the intellectual realm involves the provision of such suitable aesthetic objects. The art of poetry is primarily directed to this end.

I should like to call this immediate aspect of poetry and mathematics the aesthetic object. Its relation to the intellectual object or idea I shall call its symbolic function. Geometrical figures and sets of words, as unique objects of contemplation, are thus symbols in so far as they realize and exhibit corresponding intellectual forms.

The symbolic relation is often understood to hold between three instead of two terms. There is said to be (1) a conventional or artificial sign standing for (2) an idea, which points to (3) one or more real objects. It is hard to see the justification for the assumption in this statement that man-made things, such as signs, are different in any fundamental way from real objects. My contention is that sign and real object are equally symbolic. They both give rise to pictures, or other aesthetic objects, which show forth in their forms the intellectual object. It is not only in formulae, figures, and poems that the elements are symbols, but anything perceived suggests and exhibits ideas.

It is true that perceived things are ambiguous, that is, any one such thing suggests and exhibits many alternative ideas, but that is only because we jump from one to another symbol without noting the change in projective reference. If we held one element fixed, it would not be ambiguous in its ideal references.

Perhaps an old-fashioned theory of knowledge is relevant here. In the Continental philosophical tradition from Descartes to Kant there was a general agreement about three stages of knowledge. There were confused ideas, clear and distinct ideas, and insight or intellectual intuition. Below these three there was also recognized a chaos of feeling or sensation. Baumgarten identified the confused ideas as aesthetic objects, and the clear and distinct ideas as intellectual objects. Baumgarten's terms were dictated by the analogy with vision. The mathematical analogy with fields of projection would be appropriate and more explicit. Objects are vaguely perceived in sensation or feeling. They are partially clarified in the process of picture-making by projection or some other appropriate transformation and the resulting pictures are confused ideas, or aesthetic objects, in which distortion and design are present. When they take on the ideal reference, which I have called the symbolic function, they exhibit also the clear and distinct ideas which I have called intellectual objects. Ambiguity marks the difficulty of the first clarification. Ordered projection overcomes this by differentiating and ordering the pictures until they become focused on their respective ideas.

All this is well exemplified in the various ways of reading poetry.

139

There is the emotional school whose devotees recollect emotions and imagery on the occasion of following the lines of a poem. They go in for feeling and sensation. Then there is the aesthetic school, whose members select merely some aspect of rhythm, verbal music, or even the spacing of words, lines and capital letters. They can read the list of stations on a Continental railway with pure appreciation of its poetry, or the *Odyssey* for its roar and thunder. Finally there is the intellectual school who go from science to morals by way of metaphysics on the occasion of seeing a "flower in the crannied wall." The more dogmatic members of the school believe they can read poetry without emotion or imagery.

This is all quite obvious in the case of poetry, but it is a shock to find oneself reading mathematics from such points of view. Leibniz said he began by tasting the pleasant bits scattered here and there in mathematical treatises, and began composing his own differential calculus before he had studied either Euclid or Descartes thoroughly and analytically. He was ashamed when he met Huyghens because he had missed some simple points on the disciplinary side. Mathematics does contain many "pleasant bits." For the properly tuned eye there are many aesthetic objects even apart from geometrical figures. In the transformation of the equations of analytic geometry there is a free play of the imagination in perhaps an unrecognized harmony with the concepts of the understanding. It is true that x, y, $=$, $+$, et cetera, by themselves are opaque and uninteresting aesthetically, but the visual-intellectual aspect of an equation has significant form even for the person who has no analytical training. There is a "purposiveness without a purpose," a "disinterested interest," the two properties of the aesthetic object according to Kant, in $a^2 + b^2 = c^2$ even for one who does not know that it is the fundamental equation in trigonometry. Proportions are fascinating even to a small child. Nine-tenths of the skill with number and formulae in professional mathematical technique is due to an aesthetic appreciation of symbolic form. It is achieved in the same manner that the appreciation of sculpture and music is attained. The position of words in a poem, the network of lines in a figure, the flow of terms in a formula, present qualities and values as truly as the flight of birds, the frost figures on the windowpane, or the march of moon and stars across the sky.

It is this fitness of things, both artificial and natural, to express ideas that gives plausibility to the mysteries of ritual and the universe. Religious ritual and natural process imitate the manipulations of things by which the playwright and actor create the illusion of the stage. Science is an apt pupil in this school of natural dramaturgy whose most familiar precursors were alchemy and astrology. The aesthetic properties of ceremony, formula, natural processes are intimations of complex and profound intellectual objects, but the difficulties in intellectual clarification and discrimination leave the mind in various attitudes of belief. For every intellectual object, half-comprehended, there is an aesthetic object before which we bow in more or less deep reverence. Pure aesthetic contemplation and complete intellectual clarity are seldom found in human beings, and any middle ground is touched with credulity and idolatry.

Ultimately the difficulty of clarification becomes impossibility. For the only method we have of isolating the symbol and articulating it with the idea is transformation by analogy, of which projection in geometry is a special case. We can take the word, or the thing, and break it up into parts and say that the relation of one part of the symbol to another is the same as the relation of one part of the idea to another. Thus we isolate and identify one relation in each, but the rest of the symbol remains confused. Further, the analogy by which this is done is itself another symbol with its own confusions and mysteries. Mathematics is as much a case of this as poetry. In despair of explanation we are driven to new analogies or new symbolic statements and a molehill becomes a mountain of significance.

As a matter of fact no explanation is needed. The coincidence of of symbol and idea is an insight, a happy outcome for any intellectual process. In place of explanation there is continuous criticism of symbols. Symbols are metaphors or condensed analogies. They may be expanded into allegorical networks in which the relations may be distinguished and abstracted. Then more adequate symbols for these relations may be introduced by poet or mathematician. A critic again expands the resulting formula and new relations are discovered and again symbolized. So goes the life of reason from aesthetic object to intellectual object, gathering precious treasures of insight for the empirical scientist and man of action to use and enjoy.

The extraordinary position and power of proportions in mathematics and the essential metaphorical character of poetry are thus not mere accidents of history, but the key to an inward dialectic of thought. It is by expansion of metaphor that fact becomes intelligible, the world measured, and the complexities of experience described in language. Any history of thought might begin and end with the statement that man is an analogical animal.

THE SHIFT OF ATTENTION in mathematics from ratios and proportions to functions has had many important consequences, or if you like, there have been corresponding shifts of attention in other fields. It has become increasingly obvious in the last few years that science is abandoning its single-minded devotion to mechanics and its appropriate methods of investigation for a new and apparently more flexible set of ideas. Some see in this an emancipation from the dogmatic determinism of physics, and jump to the analogy of the biological organism. Others fear that it is a return to the pre-mechanistic theological attitude of mind and a consequent loss of skeptical rigor. Still others think of it as an impressionistic movement in science catching up with similar movements in art. As I see it, it is another case of the Pythagorean exploitation of mathematical forms. It is the latest betrothal of mathematics and poetry.

The mathematician has again been lured to an adventure with a symbolic hobbyhorse and has discovered new routes to the absolute or infinite. After a trial journey he has come back to earth and sets a new fashion in intellectual locomotion. The new vehicle feels like an airplane supported only by thin air, but the view from the rider's seat is familiar even though it involves distortions of the old perspective. Newly discovered abstractions always have an exotic manner.

Pythagoras and his disciples discovered certain numerical relations. Before they knew what they were doing, they had duplicated these relations and imputed them to geometry, calling the result magnitude. They again duplicated them and imputed them to musical instruments and sounds and called the result harmony. The accumulation was projected on the starry sky and the result was the harmony of the spheres. The process was so swift that they condensed their language and said that the world was a realm of numbers.

They had confused numbering numbers and numbered numbers. As we have seen, counting involves at least two similar series. Pythagoras saw not only two, but many more, and then said that they were all identical with the first. This was real and the rest of the world was confused experience, or prime matter. He might have done otherwise. Geometrical Pythagoreans saw the multiplication of triangles and said the world was a realm of triangles. It is an easy trick. Take any formula, find a similar form or some material that is plastic, select a suitable analogy, condense the analogy to a metaphor, take the metaphor literally, and you have a scientific philosophy. It has been done with less rigorous formulae than those of arithmetic and geometry. Thus mechanism came from the proportion, the Daltonian atom from weights and measures of the laboratory, the solar system from conic sections, Bohr's atom from the solar system, Marxian theory of history from mechanics and Christian theology.

Quite recently we have been invited to imagine movement without forces and mass, and qualities without substances. For some time the psychologist had been doing without soul and mind, and the political scientist without the sovereign state. The shock of all this is somewhat like the state of mind produced by Laplace's famous remark that he did not need God in physics. This is what happens when the mathematical physicist changes his mind, that is, his analogies.

In the present case he has been keeping company with the modern Pythagoreans. They have been analogizing with functions and the physicist has been giving us his account of their sayings. In describing functions they have been saying that for any value of the variable there is a corresponding value of the function. The physicist has asked the traditional question: What varies? and the Pythagorean has answered laconically: Everything, even the function is a variable. The so-called constants are only relations governing the variations, and even these so-called constants are only arbitrarily fixed by reference to still other merely arbitrary constants. Even the numbers are thus relative.

This would have been bad news in the seventeenth century, but since that time the physicist has been watching electrical phenomena and trying to keep his accounts straight in the old terms of proportions and equations where constants were constant. But latterly the ratios have slipped and the accounts have got tangled up. The numbers seem to be elastic. Forces, masses, and weights won't stay put. The elements begin to move about on the Mendeleeff chart. The old method of calculating errors of measurement seems to signify more than human and material imperfection. It is therefore good news now that mathematics has an analogous, but clearer notion to offer to the scientist. So the physicist has translated the language of the mathematician into his own terms and has had some terms such as mass, substance, force, or cause, left over. These he threw overboard and the accounts begin to come out straight again. The mathematics is now verified by observation. The new analogies work.

The result sounds like the biologist's description of organisms. They too are forms undergoing apparently significant variation in every part. Life is an equilibrium of changes. Animals were for a time compared with machines, but with very meager results. Now the whole physical universe is compared to an organism with apparently great results. The physical universe is an organism of organisms. Or not to throw over the old tradition too quickly, the world is an organic mechanism. Biological function and mathematical function are the same. The analogy has been condensed, and the resulting metaphor is metaphysical truth. It spreads to psychology which needed it badly and, with suitable revisions, we have *Gestalten* or forms devouring the faculties of the soul, the complexes of the psyche, and the reflexes of the nervous system. It becomes a philosophy of life in emergent evolution. Pythagoras has another reincarnation in which the former rooster has become the superman.

Mathematics and poetry, as forms of thought, have a peculiar property which I have called expansiveness. They are always restless and hungry for more. Sometimes this has the aspect of the search for an absolute. In mathematics the appearance of this aspect is the sign of the completion of a symbolic episode, and the imminence of a new extension in the direction of greater generality. In poetry it is the sign of a religious and mystical peace and acquiescence. At other times expansiveness wears an air of piety to a tradition and devotes itself to the task of refinement and assimilation of detail. Both of these in terms of logic are the play of ultimate categories such as sameness and difference, one and many, and the being and not-being of negation and affirmation. A dialectical investigation of these, such as Plato made, would show that the play and consequently the expansion of ideas is unlimited except by the energy and inclination of thinking beings. Some have found in this a metaphysical secret.

There is a recurrent aphorism in philosophy that summarizes this feature of thought. It says that reality is a sphere having an infinite radius and a center at every point. I mentioned this in connection with the generalization of the notion of projective fields made by Bruno and Leibniz, and I might have added some of the dark remarks of Einstein about the shape of the universe. The saying is not wholly nonsensical; its principle of order can be stated.

The infinite sphere denotes a series of spheres each of which represents a stage of mathematical discovery. A set of assumptions is laid down and developed by deductive and intuitive methods into a system. The system so generated is a finite sphere. As soon as it is sufficiently developed, there is discovered an underlying set of assumptions with a larger system than the former as its consequence. When this is developed, it is a sphere including the former as one of its dependent parts. Modern multidimensional geometry thus includes Euclidean geometry. This latter sphere is in turn a subdivision of a still more inclusive sphere, and the expansive process apparently never ends. The study of comparative literature shows similarly ordered sets of allegories.

This is the cultural macrocosm. The microcosm of the individual mind is similar, and the corresponding series of spheres is an intellectual biography, a mind in the making.

We can be more explicit. The infinity of these spheres is suggestive of the number system with its densities, compactnesses, and continuities. The paradoxes of counting are solved by correlating the members of one series with those of another. We can bring a similar analogical calculus to bear on the series of mathematical and poetical spheres.

Mathematics deals with relations, and poetry deals with qualities. A sphere results when we can see the *relations* holding between *qualities*. Then the two series can be correlated. Mathematical functions find elementary values in qualities. Qualities find their relations in the functions of mathematics. Whenever this happens, a system is recognized, and it takes on a quasi-independence and reality. Often the effect in the thinker is a conviction. Belief attaches itself only to such systems. The further expansions and the wider assumptions are ignored and there is a resting point for thought in a mathe-matico-poetic allegory.

This is the secret of the drama which at its best undercuts the scientific and religious attitude of mind. Consequently the best metaphysical criticism of mathematics and poetry is to be found in the drama and the novel. Tragedy and comedy are the classic modes of treatment of this theme. Their analysis will exhibit it further.

The fundamental notions in tragedy are called *hybris* and *nemesis*. The first is the attitude of arrogance or insolence that arises from blindness in human nature. The second is the eventual consequence of that blindness and arrogance, the vengeance that the ignored factor in a situation takes on man and his virtues. These are moralistic terms but the intellectualistic transformation is easy. It can be performed on the terms of Aristotle's analysis of tragedy.

A tragic character must have besides hybris, the virtue of irony. This quality is the exercise of the capacity to discover and systematize clear ideas. It appears at first as a naïve idealism that makes it impos-sible to take circumstances at their face value, and expresses itself in a kind of satirical questioning, such as that of Socrates. Accompany-ing it is a sense of humor which condenses and dispels intervening fogs. At bottom it is a faith that there are ideas to be discovered and a conviction that the task is not easy. St. Francis and Don Quixote are additional good examples in literature. Dramatic tragedy usually dis-closes such a character in some advanced stage when the idea is in sight, so that action is understood as aiming to achieve its clarification. This is the situation presented in the prologue.

Action moves on exemplifying and expanding the idea. Even at this point there are at least two possible interpretations of the events. One is held by the audience who usually know the outcome already. The other is that held by the hero who is possessed of the idea to such an extent that he builds up a separate story or interpretation for himself in conformity with his ideal. Events pile up and are turned to his account by the alchemy of his own rationality. The situation becomes complicated and each event is charged with dramatic foreshadowing. The hero sees dilemmas in everything and sticks to his course in spite of the oppositions. His determination finally reaches desperation. This is the complication of the situation and the advent of hybris.

At length he is faced with some crucial and unavoidable predicament. He must decide. Using all his intellectual powers he makes the only decision possible on his interpretation of the situation. This is the crisis. In terms of mathematics and poetry, he has developed a system of relations, his idea; and the events have supplied a corresponding set of qualities. The situation is a full-rounded sphere.

Events come faster and pile themselves high on either side of his chosen path. They now have a threatening aspect for him, but there is no turning back. There is a dull inevitability about them. Finally they break and all is ruin with no compensating circumstance. This is the reversal of circumstance and catastrophe. The rounded sphere of apparent success is in a thousand pieces.

Then if he has the true quality of irony there is a recognition of what he had ignored. There comes the still small voice in the calm following the thunder and the earthquake, the voice of a god speaking not words of pity or revenge, but the decrees of necessity on his situation and his idea. Both are thrown upon a vaster background than he had envisaged, the doings of fate. In these decrees there is light and the hero recognizes himself, his idea, and his plight in terms of laws that are not for yesterday, today or tomorrow, but for always. This is the purgation.

But this may be only one episode, the first of a trilogy. The same hero, or another implicated character goes on into the new sphere with the new version of the eternal verities. No man should be judged happy until he is dead.

This pattern is the Greek view of life. It is the method of their and our science, history, and philosophy. In it poetry becomes criticism of life. It is, I believe, the final metaphysical conclusion of Greek philosophy in Plato and Aristotle.

The Greek employment of it had been humanistic in the main. The Greek tragic hero was a typical man isolated and projected on a background of fate. The late middle ages and the Renaissance substituted natural objects for the heroes of vicarious tragedies, the experiments in the laboratory. They put such objects under controlled conditions, introduced artificial complications, and waited for the answering pronouncement of fate. The crucial experiment is the crisis of an attempt to rationalize experience, that is, to force it into our analogies. Purgation and recognition are now called elimination of false hypotheses and verification. The shift is significant, but the essential tragic pattern of tragedy is still there. The popularizer of science is inviting us to reverse the change and rehumanize tragedy. There is some doubt whether he knows what he is proposing.

Tragedy proceeds by analogy and homogeneous substitution in the rationalizing thought of the hero. Events are prepared, "controlled," willed, interpreted, so as to be consistent with the idea or hypothesis. The direction of expansion is integration and generality. It ends in a cumulative catastrophe and a general purgation. Comedy seems to provide another method. It proceeds by wide variation and heterogeneous substitution. Every turn in the action marks an inconsistency discovered, a plan gone wrong, a platitude rendered paradoxical, a principle disproved, a fact caught in duplicity. There is expansion here also, but in the phase of discrimination and distinction-making. The hero of a comedy must see the point of every joke or of none, so that all the ideas may have equal opportunity for conflict and continual purgation. In a good comedy every idea must be deflated and purged by the ordeal of laughter. One laughs with or at the hero who exposes them and himself to the comic purgation.

Of course, there are many kinds of comedy, each type depending on some one of the types of heterogeneous substitution. There is the pun based on verbal substitution, the practical joke ranging from slapstick to farcical humor based on substitutions of actions for words or ideas. Finally, there is the comedy of manners based on the substitution of ideas. This can be illustrated in mathematics.

In the study of functions and their properties it is customary to substitute trial values for one variable at a time and watch the result in the values taken on by the other variables and the whole function in consequence. By a series of such trials the limiting values are found. This is the Greek method of solving equations and was revived in analytic geometry for the purpose of isolating the general properties of equations. It is also used in the calculus and the theory of functions. McClaurin substituted zero for x in Taylor's Series and discovered the method for expanding any function by using derivative functions. The study of maxima and minima, or the greatest and least values of functions, is another application. In general the unusual or unique values are substituted. Sometimes the result is an indeterminate or nonsensical expression, and sometimes it is a transformation into another class of functions whose unsuspected relations to the original class are thus discovered. The mathematical result is, as in the comedy of literature, a clarification and definition of the properties of the ideas involved.

The main points in the comparison of the forms of tragedy and comedy, and their modern descendants in drama and fiction, also the operation of the principles of substitution and expansion that relate them, may be seen in three versions of the Oedipus story.

The first is the Sophoclean argument:

The god, Apollo, has made it known through the Oracle at Delphi that the son of Laius, King of Thebes, will kill his father and marry Jocasta, his mother. In accordance with the Greek practice with regard to the pronouncements of the Oracle Laius plans to circumvent the divine decree by having his son Oedipus exposed. A shepherd is given the commission to dispose of the child. But he is touched by pity and hands him over to the care of another shepherd, who in turn passes him on to Polybus, King of Corinth, in whose house Oedipus is reared as heir to the Corinthian throne. As a grown man he hears a rumor that he is not the son of his apparent parents. He starts to Delphi to find out his true origin. On the way he meets a royal chariot, and is pushed off the narrow road by its attendants. He attacks the occupant, kills him, and the attendants also, except one who escapes.

Proceeding on his way, in due time he nears Thebes, which is mourning the death of its king. He who can answer the riddle of the Sphinx will be made king. Oedipus answers the riddle, is made king, and becomes famous for his just rule. Soon there are reports of a plague in the city of Thebes, and King Oedipus sends to the Delphic Oracle to learn its cause. The answer comes that the plague is punishment for a crime committed in the city. As soon as the offender is found and punished, the plague will disappear. The King imposes a penalty, exile, and curses the guilty. The investigation proceeds without result. Oedipus intensifies the search, and a rumor starts that he himself is the offender. He accuses his brother-in-law, Creon, of plotting to seize the throne for himself. The blind seer Teiresias is called in to arbitrate. He confirms the rumor against Oedipus and is accused of a lying conspiracy with Creon.

Finally, the escaped attendant on Laius' chariot is called in to describe the murderer of the former king. It is still uncertain, and the shepherds are sought. They convince Oedipus that he is guilty of incest and murdering his father. He puts out his own eyes, and Jocasta hangs herself. Blind Oedipus and his daughter, Antigone, go into exile to free the city of the plague.

The comic version might go as follows:

A shepherd has come to Thebes to celebrate a short vacation from sheep-watching. He is making merry with wine and old friends. They tell him about the death of the king and encourage him to answer the riddle of the Sphinx. In his state of inebriation and spiritual ecstasy he accidentally hits upon the right answer. He is taken to the court and made king of Thebes, by this time sober and embarrassed. He marries Jocasta.

In the course of time the ceremonies and royal duties begin to bore him. He plans to escape. The plague comes to Thebes. He sends an old shepherd friend as messenger to Delphi, instructing him before he leaves what his report is to be. The shepherd returns and says that the King is Oedipus, Laius' son, who escaped exposure, and has fulfilled the prophecy that he would kill his father and marry his mother. There is danger that the King and Queen will be stoned by the people.

Meanwhile Jocasta has fallen in love with the shepherd and is also bored with court life. The herald reports that she has hanged herself, and as they carry out a dummy corpse to show the people, the King and Queen escape by another route to the hills where they tend sheep in peace.

A modern novel:

King Laius of Thebes is loved by his people for his strong and just administration of the laws, but he has a bad temper. In a fit of temper brought on by some insubordination of his own six-year-old son, Oedipus, he bursts a blood vessel and dies. A regency is declared until Oedipus is old enough to take on his father's duties. Creon, the brother of Jocasta, the queen, becomes regent. Oedipus is sent to be educated at the Persian court.

At the age of twenty-one he returns, a man of the world, but in ill health. He is loved by the people because they think his ill health is due to his grief for his father, also because he reminds them of his father in his passion for justice. He marries the Princess of the house of Corinth, who also wins the hearts of the people because she resembles Jocasta, their former queen.

Some years later there is a plague in Thebes. The people are going blind. Oedipus' wife is a victim and dies. The Oracle is consulted and its answer is that the cause of the blindness is a mysterious Persian disease that has spread from the palace itself to the town. Oedipus hands over the throne to Haemon, the son of Creon, with whom Antigone, Oedipus' daughter, is in love. Antigone will not marry him for fear of continuing the plague. Oedipus grows blind, and Antigone devotes the rest of her life to caring for her father in a country home near Thebes. Haemon comes often to see her.

Oedipus dies calling for his mother and the sun.

Critical philosophy is the highest type of intellectual comedy, and Plato is the best comic poet of philosophy. It is said that Plato as a youth wrote comedies for the Olympic prizes. The plays are lost, but the marks of the comic poet are to be found in his dialogues. For in them we find all the types of humor bent to the somewhat tragic purpose of a moral philosophy. He is a master of heterogeneous substitution, and in the mouth of Socrates such substitutions get the sparkling expression that comedy should provide.

All the persons of the drama speak in character. In the early dialogues Socrates is talking with Sophists of one sort or another. He catches them making comic substitutions without a smile, usually aping a tragic *deus ex machina* in their manner and matter. He takes up the game and carries it to the extremes where the pun or witticism can be seen. These first dialogues should be read with one eye on the comic poet George Bernard Shaw, in whom the same Platonic blend of comedy and tragedy is articulate.

In the *Republic* Plato is exposing the Pythagorean secrets of the Delphic Oracle, which is the Greek analogue of our modern research foundations. It expounded the mathematical and poetic secrets of the universe in moral precepts for the people. In the later dialogues the theory of ideas, a common doctrine of the day and the pet device of Socrates to confound his opponents, undergoes the ordeal by laughter. The humor becomes more intellectual and abstract, and the sparkle becomes the play of philosophic insights. Poetry and mathematics meet and part in perfect freedom and lack of mutual embarrassment. Most of the dialogues end with an epilogue, the first part of which is mathematics, and the second part of which a poetic myth. Many have misunderstood these endings and taken the myth as the final interpretation of the mathematics. They do Plato a great injustice. His only conclusions are the clear and distinct ideas that his comic treatment reveals in unsuspected turns of the dialogues.

But comedy plays with the ideas to which tragedy has given birth. It is never the discoverer or creator. Plato's philosophy never quite frees its doctrines from their traditional origins, although it does give them an ideal dimension. The play of ideas is always hedged about with the darkness and mystery of tragic issues. This is inevitable. There probably never was a pure comedy or tragedy. The drama is often spoiled by a bad mixture of the two. Ibsen tried to fill comic situations with fate. Comic characters strut across the stage inflating the comedy, the play of local customs and popular science, with a pseudo-seriousness. This is the tragicomedy of the melodrama and contains a sentimental faith and a preaching hero. It is an unconscious parody on tragic purgation.

Ibsen on the other hand is an authentic historian, and the times he describes are not remote from the present. Most of us live with the mixture of poetry and mathematics in our heads which makes our understanding melodramatic. Our romanticism and our realism are seldom purged. One reason for this is that science is being preached to us before it is understood by the preachers. We apply it without irony and study it without humor. The consequence is sentimentalism in our action and mystification at the dénouement.

It is this situation that has aroused the present controversy over the popularization of science. It is a typical crisis in the life of reason. Reason oscillates between tragic pain and comic disillusionment. The popularizer is speaking seriously for the method of the laboratory. He is the stage manager for the world and wishes people to act and speak by the book of science. If his management were successful there would be the crisis in civilization which he foretells and fears. Whether there are enough tragic heroes to give it a high seriousness, nobody knows. But it seems at present that the actors have missed the spirit of the play. Most of them are melodramatic heroes and villains who now and then suffer comic relief. There are here and there signs of the play of clear and distinct ideas that go with comedy. There are a few individuals with insight and love of ideas, who understand without believing. But on the whole science is not yet a tradition within which one can play. The result is a confusion of mathematics and poetry in experience that I pointed out at the beginning.

It would be a pleasant prospect if this essay were an introduction to a *De Rerum Natura* or a *Divine Comedy*. When such a work is worthily done it will be clear what the difference between tragedy and comedy is. It will then be possible to decide what to do with modern scientific opinion. It is said that the function of theology has always been to spiritualize the sacraments, that is, to discover and formulate their symbolic function and to reduce popular belief in their causal efficacy to its proper status. The function of philosophical criticism is to intellectualize scientific method, that is, to discover and formulate its symbolic significance and to reduce popular belief in its causal efficacy to its proper status. With regard to the symbolic function of science and its conclusions, at present it can only be said that they are wavering shadows of those clear and distinct ideas without which experience is neither good nor true. Their present mathematical and poetic embodiments are intimations of some such immortality.

KEYSTONE BOOKS

Keystone Short Stories

COLOR OF DARKNESS by James Purdy (KB-25)
THE GAMES OF NIGHT by Stig Dagerman (KB-26)
THE DIGNITY OF NIGHT by Klaus Roehler (KB-27)
WHITE APPLES by Arno Karlen (KB-29)
THE SWING by Vera Cacciatore (KB-30)
THE GO-AWAY BIRD by Muriel Spark (KB-31)
TELL ME A RIDDLE by Tillie Olsen (KB-32)
THE END OF PITY by Robie Macauley (KB-39)
THE LAST HUSBAND by William Humphrey (KB-40)
HAPPY FAMILIES ARE ALL ALIKE by Peter Taylor (KB-41)

NEW WORLD WRITING 16 (KB-17)
NEW WORLD WRITING 17 (KB-20)
NEW WORLD WRITING 18 (KB-24)
NEW WORLD WRITING 19 (KB-33)
NEW WORLD WRITING 20 (KB-42)

THE ART OF MAKING SENSE by Lionel Ruby (KB-15)
MORE IN ANGER by Marya Mannes (KB-16)
THE ART SPIRIT by Robert Henri (KB-18)
GUY DOMVILLE by Henry James (with biographical chapters by Leon Edel) (KB-19)
RELIGION AND THE MODERN MIND by W. T. Stace (KB-21)
THE PICARESQUE SAINT by R. W. B. Lewis (KB-28)
POETRY AND MATHEMATICS by Scott Buchanan (KB-43)
THE PILGRIMAGE OF WESTERN MAN by Stringfellow Barr (KB-45)

Keystone Discographies

THE COLLECTOR'S BACH by Nathan Broder (KB-3)

THE COLLECTOR'S JAZZ: *Traditional and Swing* by John S. Wilson (KB-4)

THE COLLECTOR'S HAYDN by C. G. Burke (KB-7)

THE COLLECTOR'S CHOPIN AND SCHUMANN by Harold C. Schonberg (KB-8)

THE COLLECTOR'S TCHAIKOVSKY AND THE FIVE by John Briggs (KB-9)

THE COLLECTOR'S JAZZ: *Modern* by John S. Wilson (KB-10)

THE COLLECTOR'S TWENTIETH-CENTURY MUSIC IN THE WESTERN HEMISPHERE by Arthur Cohn (KB-23)

THE COLLECTOR'S VERDI AND PUCCINI by Max de Schauensee (KB-46)

THE COLLECTOR'S BEETHOVEN by John Briggs (KB-47)

Keystone Western Americana

THE LEWIS AND CLARK EXPEDITION by Meriwether Lewis (3 vols.) (KB-34, -35, -36)

ASTORIA by Washington Irving (2 vols.) (KB-37, -38)

COMMERCE OF THE PRAIRIES by Josiah Gregg (2 vols.) (KB-52, -53)

MOUNTAINS AND MOLEHILLS by Frank Marryat (KB-49)

THE PERSONAL NARRATIVE OF JAMES O. PATTIE (KB-50)

THREE YEARS AMONG THE INDIANS AND MEXICANS by Thomas James (KB-51)

Keystone Books in Medicine

EPILEPSY: *What It Is and What to Do About It* by Tracy J. Putnam, M.D. (KB-1)

LIVING WITH YOUR ALLERGY by Samuel M. Feinberg, M.D. (KB-2)

HELP FOR TEN MILLION: *Arthritis, Rheumatism and Gout* by Darrell C. Crain, M.D. (KB-5)

CATHARTICS AND COMMON SENSE by William Farrar, M.D. (KB-6)

HEARING LOSS by Greydon G. Boyd, M.D. (KB-11)

HIGH BLOOD PRESSURE by Eugene B. Mozes, M.D. (KB-12)

PARKINSON'S DISEASE by Lewis J. Doshay, M.D. (KB-13)

WILL MY HEART FAIL? by William A. Jeffers, M.D. (KB-14)

YOU AND YOURS: *How to Help Older People* by Julietta K. Arthur (KB-22)